KB004939

My First Writing Practice In Korean

매일매일 한국어 쓰기 연습

My First Writing Practice In Korean

매일매일 한국어 쓰기 연습

1판 1쇄 · 1st edition published	2022. 8. 1.
1판 3쇄 · 3rd edition published	2023. 2. 27.

지은이 · Written by	Talk To Me In Korean
책임편집 · Edited by	선경화 Kyunghwa Sun, 석다혜 Dahye Seok
디자인 · Designed by	이은정 Eunjeong Lee
일러스트레이션 · Illustrations by	이은정 Eunjeong Lee
디자인 총괄 · Design directed by	선윤아 Yoona Sun
녹음 · Voice recordings by	김희주 Heeju Kim
펴낸곳 · Published by	롱테일북스 Longtail Books
펴낸이 · Publisher	이수영 Su Young Lee
편집 · Copy-edited by	김보경 Florence Kim
주소 · Address	04033 서울특별시 마포구 양화로 113, 3층(서교동, 순흥빌딩) 3rd Floor, 113 Yanghwa-ro, Mapo-gu, Seoul, KOREA
이메일 · E-mail	TTMIK@longtailbooks.co.kr
ISBN	979-11-91343-53-3 13710

TTMIK - TALK TO ME IN KOREAN

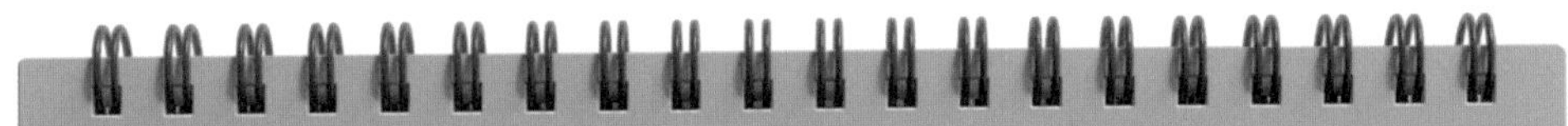

My First Writing Practice In Korean

매일매일 한국어 쓰기 연습

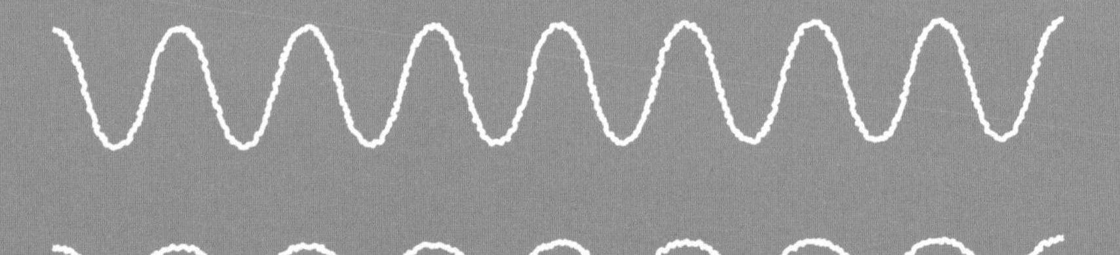

TABLE OF CONTENTS

Preface

As a Korean learner, how often do you get to use your Korean skills? Even if you do not have a Korean tutor or many Korean friends to speak with, a sure-fire way exists to actively use your Korean — social media!

We have designed this book to help you utilize what you learned so far and form practical Korean sentences that have real meaning and value for you. You have already learned diverse grammar points and vocabulary words. It's time to actually use them!

What was your day like today? What is on your mind right now? What kind of achievement are you celebrating today? After studying with this book, you will be able to confidently express these thoughts in Korean!

How to Use This Book

Each "DAY" introduces a short expression structure that you can use on social media or in your journal. We'll call this a key structure from now on.

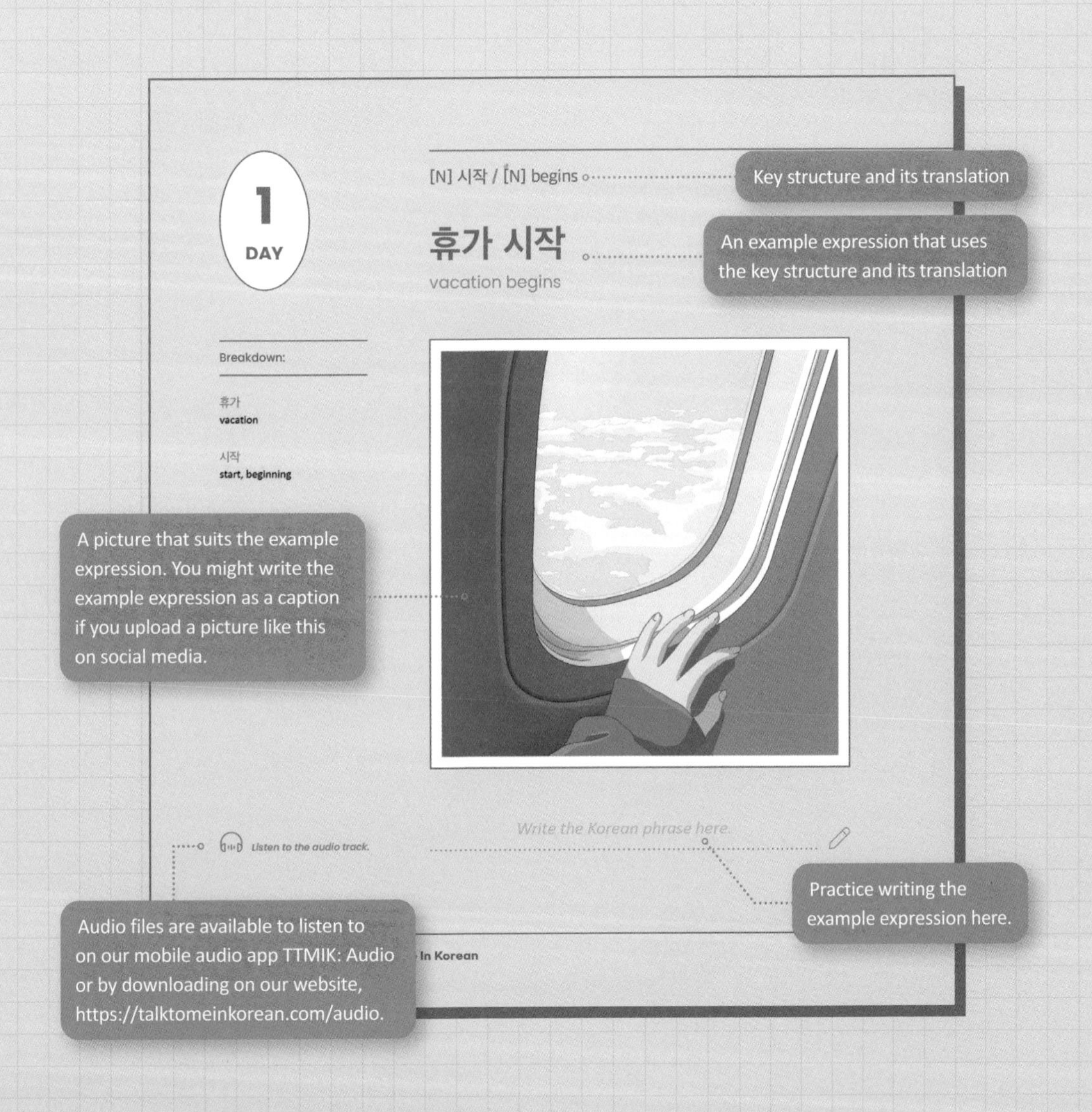

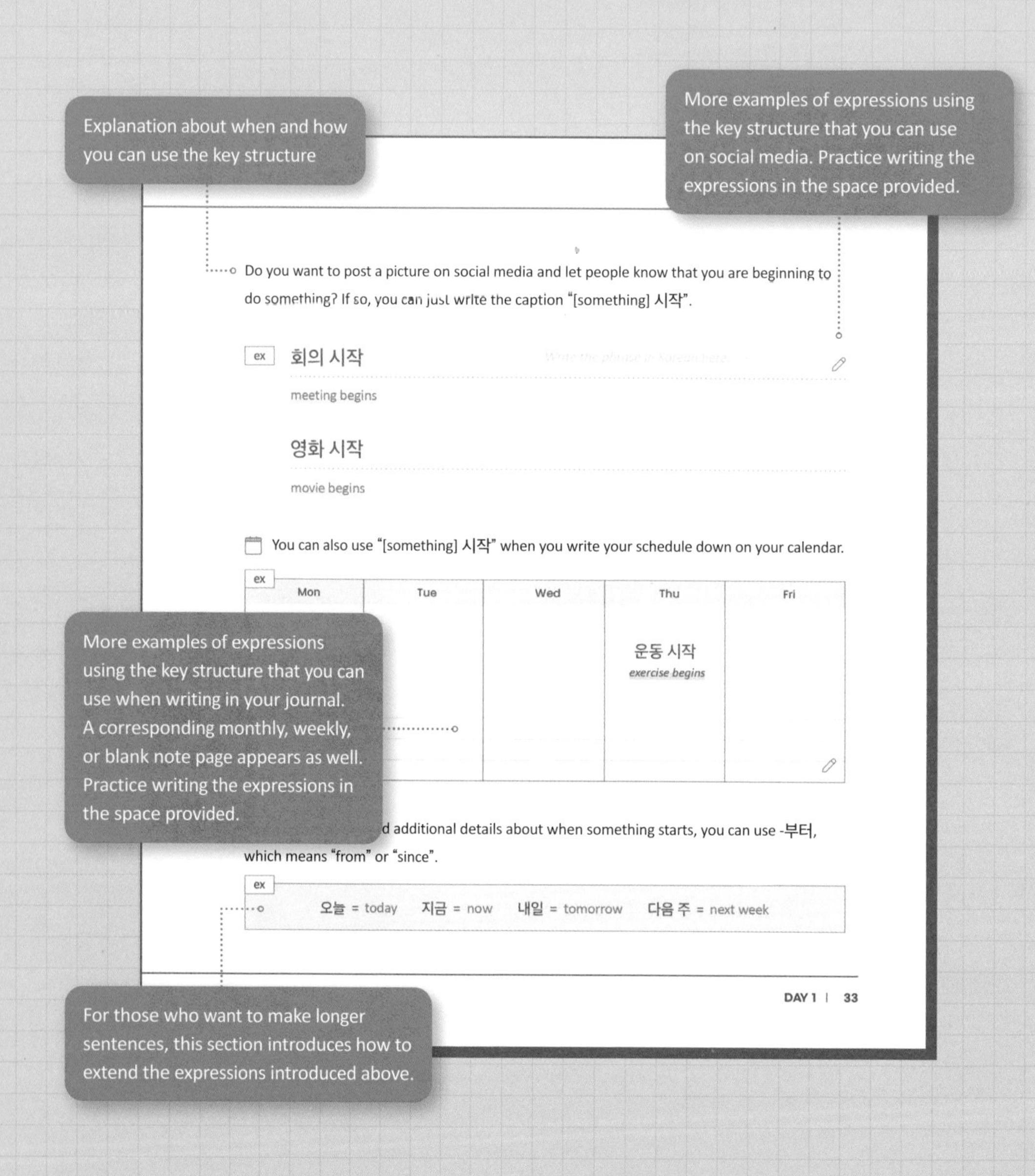
Explanation about when and how you can use the key structure
More examples of expressions using the key structure that you can use on social media. Practice writing the expressions in the space provided.
Do you want to post a picture on social media and let people know that you are beginning to do something? If so, you can just write the caption "[something] 시작".
ex
회의 시작
meeting begins
영화 시작
movie begins
You can also use "[something] 시작" when you write your schedule down on your calendar.
Mon
Tue
Wed
Thu
Fri
운동 시작
exercise begins
More examples of expressions using the key structure that you can use when writing in your journal. A corresponding monthly, weekly, or blank note page appears as well. Practice writing the expressions in the space provided.
d additional details about when something starts, you can use -부터, which means "from" or "since".
오늘 = today
지금 = now
내일 = tomorrow
다음 주 = next week
DAY 1 | 33
For those who want to make longer sentences, this section introduces how to extend the expressions introduced above.

DAY 1

오늘부터 휴가 시작

my vacation begins today

지금부터 회의 시작

the meeting begins now

내일부터 방학 시작

my school vacation starts tomorrow

다음 주부터 운동 시작

I will start exercising next week

If you would like to change the noun phrases above into complete sentences, you can use either 시작이다 or 시작한다.

오늘부터 휴가 시작이다. *Today is the start of vacation.*	오늘부터 휴가 시작한다. *My vacation starts today.*
지금부터 회의 시작이다. *It is now the beginning of the meeting.*	지금부터 회의 시작한다. *The meeting starts now.*

...t Writing Practice In Korean

Practice writing the expressions in the space provided.

For those who are wondering how to write the expressions above in complete sentences, examples of full sentences are introduced here.

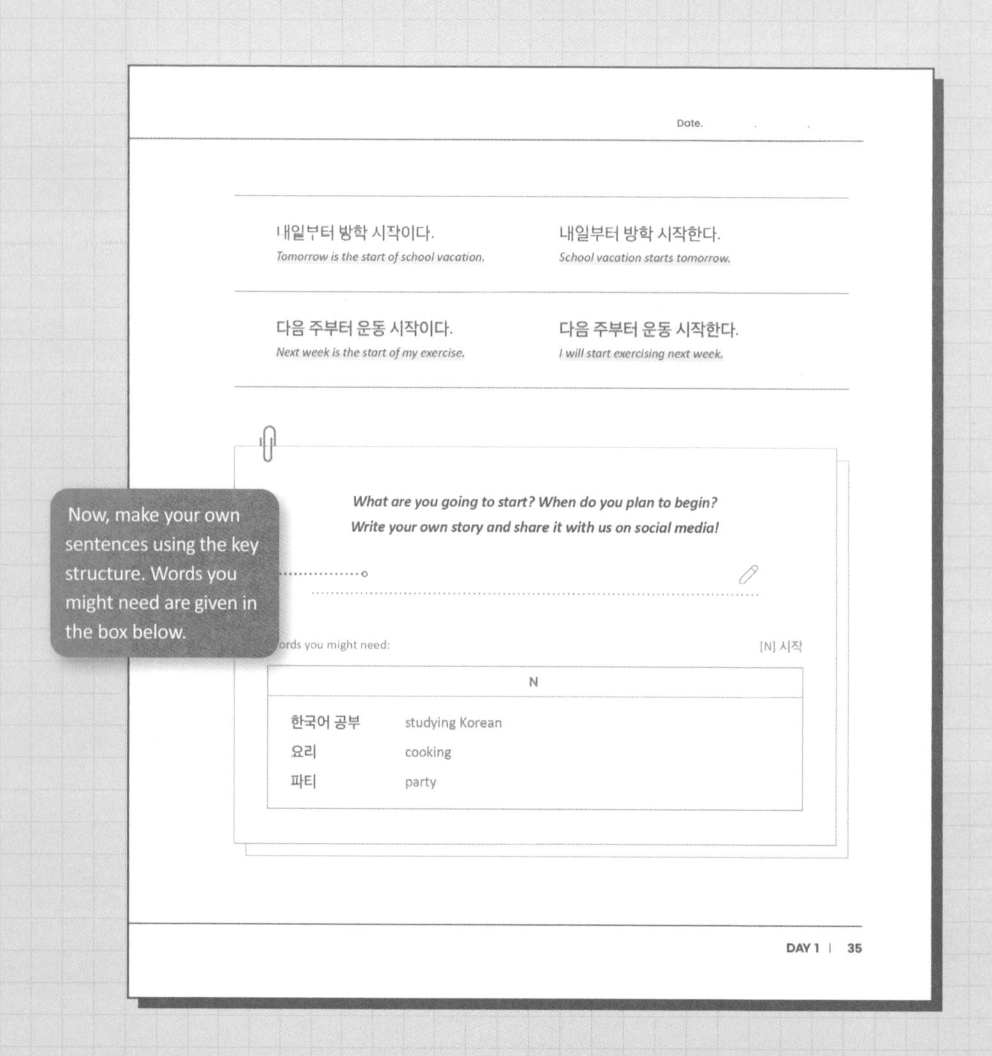
Date. . .
내일부터 방학 시작이다.
Tomorrow is the start of school vacation.
내일부터 방학 시작한다.
School vacation starts tomorrow.
다음 주부터 운동 시작이다.
Next week is the start of my exercise.
다음 주부터 운동 시작한다.
I will start exercising next week.
What are you going to start? When do you plan to begin?
Write your own story and share it with us on social media!
Now, make your own sentences using the key structure. Words you might need are given in the box below.
ords you might need:
[N] 시작
N
한국어 공부 studying Korean
요리 cooking
파티 party
DAY 1 | 35

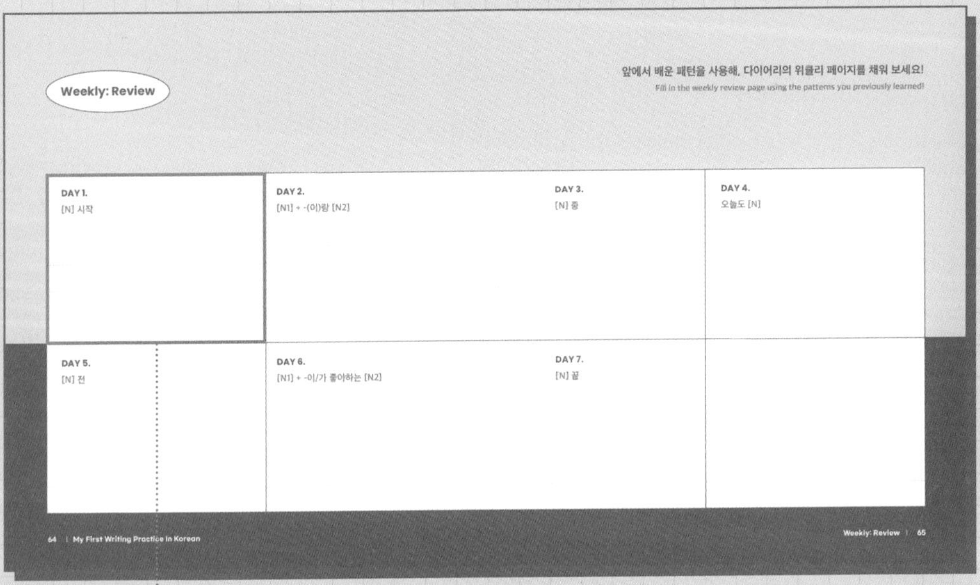

Weekly: Review

앞에서 배운 패턴을 사용해, 다이어리의 위클리 페이지를 채워 보세요!

Fill in the weekly review page using the patterns you previously learned!

DAY 1. [N] 시작	DAY 2. [N1] + -(이)랑 [N2]	DAY 3. [N] 중	DAY 4. 오늘도 [N]
DAY 5. [N] 전	DAY 6. [N1] + -이/가 좋아하는 [N2]	DAY 7. [N] 끝	

64 | My First Writing Practice in Korean

Weekly: Review | 65

DAY 1.

[N] 시작

After every seven to eight "DAY"s, you'll find a weekly review page where you can practice writing your own expressions again by using the structures you learned previously. Try filling in the expressions that relate to you.

Korean Language Basics

Sentence Endings

Narrative Sentence Ending: -(ㄴ/는)다

In Talk To Me In Korean books, you mostly come across sentences that end in -아/어/여요. In this book, however, you will find a lot of sentences that end in the formal casual verb ending -(ㄴ/는)다.

-(ㄴ/는)다 is a verb ending that you can use when narrating an incident, fact, or state. When you use -(ㄴ/는)다, what you are saying is not intended for any specific audience, but is rather just a general account of things. This is why -(ㄴ/는)다 is usually used in essay-style writing, such as in a journal, blog, or on social media.

If you write something for a specific audience, you need to be careful when you use -(ㄴ/는)다 because it is a formal CASUAL verb ending. Instead, when writing to a specific audience, you should use either the informal POLITE verb ending -아/어/여요 or the formal POLITE verb ending -(스)ㅂ니다. If you write something very casual, such as a letter to someone who is very close to you or younger than you, you can use the informal casual verb ending -아/어/여.

Conjugations

Present Tense	Action Verbs	Verb stems ending with a vowel or the consonant ㄹ (in which case ㄹ is dropped) + -ㄴ다 Ex) 시작하다 = to start 시작하 + -ㄴ다 = 시작한다 = it starts

		Ex) 팔다 = to sell 파 + -ㄴ다 = 판다 = they sell Verb stems ending with a consonant (except for the consonant ㄹ) + -는다 Ex) 굽다 = to bake 굽 + -는다 = 굽는다 = I bake
	Descriptive Verbs (= adjectives in infinitive form)	Verb stem + -다 Ex) 예쁘다 = to be pretty 예쁘 + -다 = 예쁘다 = it is pretty
	Nouns	Nouns ending with a consonant + -이다 Ex) 옷 = clothes 옷 + -이다 = 옷이다 = they are clothes
		Nouns ending with a vowel + -다 Ex) 노래 = song 노래 + -다 = 노래다 = it is a song
Past Tense	Verbs	If the vowel of the last letter of the verb stem is ㅗ or ㅏ, attach -았다. Ex) 보다 = to watch 보 + -았다 = 보았다 = 봤다 = I watched * When ㅗ and -아 are combined, they become ㅘ.

		If the vowel of the last letter of the verb stem is not ㅗ or ㅏ, attach -었다. Ex) 마시다 = to drink 마시 + -었다 = 마시었다 = 마셨다 = I drank * When ㅣ and -어 are combined, they become ㅕ.
		If the last letter of the verb stem is 하, attach -였다. Ex) 행복하다 = to be happy 행복하 + -였다 = 행복하였다 = 행복했다 = I was happy * 하였다 is almost always shortened to 했다.
	Nouns	Nouns ending with a consonant + -이었다 Ex) 끝 = end 끝 + -이었다 = 끝이었다 = it was the end
		Nouns ending with a vowel + -였다 Ex) 목표 = goal 목표 + -였다 = 목표였다 = it was a goal
Future Tense	Action Verbs	Verb stems ending with a vowel or the consonant ㄹ (in which case ㄹ is dropped) + -ㄹ 것이다 Ex) 가다 = to go 가 + -ㄹ 것이다 = 갈 것이다 = 갈 거다 = I will go

		* 것이다 is often shortened to 거다 in casual situations.
		Verb stems ending with a consonant (except for the consonant ㄹ) + -을 것이다 Ex) 읽다 = to read 읽 + -을 것이다 = 읽을 것이다 = 읽을 거다 = I will read

Basic Sentence Ending: -아/어/여요

-아/어/여요 is an informal polite verb ending used to speak to someone who is older or in a higher position than you.

Conjugations

Present Tense	If the vowel of the last letter of the verb stem is ㅗ or ㅏ, attach -아요. Ex) 좋다 = to be good 좋 + -아요 = 좋아요 = it is good
	If the vowel of the last letter of the verb stem is not ㅗ or ㅏ, attach -어요. Ex) 힘들다 = to be tough 힘들 + -어요 = 힘들어요 = it is tough

	If the last letter of the verb stem is 하, attach -여요. 하여요 is always shortened to 해요. Ex) 깨끗하다 = to be clean 깨끗하 + -여요 = 깨끗하여요 = 깨끗해요 = it is clean
Past Tense	If the vowel of the last letter of the verb stem is ㅗ or ㅏ, attach -았어요. Ex) 가다 = to go 가 + -았어요 = 갔어요 = I went * When ㅏ meets -았어요, 아 is omitted to become 갔어요, not 가았어요.
	If the vowel of the last letter of the verb stem is not ㅗ or ㅏ, attach -었어요. Ex) 맛있다 = to be delicious 맛있 + -었어요 = 맛있었어요 = it was delicious
	If the last letter of the verb stem is 하, attach -였어요. Ex) 성공하다 = to succeed 성공하 + -였어요 = 성공하였어요 = 성공했어요 = I succeeded * 하였어요 is almost always shortened to 했어요.
Future Tense	Verb stems ending with a vowel or the consonant ㄹ (in which case ㄹ is dropped) + -ㄹ 거예요 Ex) 타다 = to ride 타 + -ㄹ 거예요 = 탈 거예요 = I will ride

Verb stems ending with a consonant (except for the consonant ㄹ) + -을 거예요 Ex) 먹다 = to eat 먹 + -을 거예요 = 먹을 거예요 = I will eat

Imperative Sentence Ending: -(으)세요

-(으)세요 is used when you tell someone politely to do something.

Conjugations

Verb stems ending with a vowel or the consonant ㄹ (in which case ㄹ is dropped) + -세요 Ex) 기다리다 = to wait 기다리 + -세요 = 기다리세요 = please wait Ex) 밀다 = to push 미 + -세요 = 미세요 = please push
Verb stems ending with a consonant (except for the consonant ㄹ) + -으세요 Ex) 웃다 = to smile 웃 + -으세요 = 웃으세요 = please smile

Assumptive Question Ending: -(으)ㄹ까

-(으)ㄹ까 can used in a few different types of situations. In this book it is used to ask oneself a question or show doubt about something.

Conjugations

Verb stems ending with a vowel or the consonant ㄹ (in which case ㄹ is dropped) + -ㄹ까
Ex) 머리를 자르다 = to have one's hair cut 머리를 자르 + -ㄹ까 = 머리를 자를까 = should I have my hair cut
Verb stems ending with a consonant (except for the consonant ㄹ) + -을까
Ex) 일찍 퇴근할 수 있다 = to be able to leave work early 일찍 퇴근할 수 있 + -을까 = 일찍 퇴근할 수 있을까 = I wonder if I will be able to leave work early

Exclamative Verb Ending: -네(요)

-네(요) is used to express your surprise at or impression of something.

Ex) 벌써 끝이네. = Wow, it is already the end.
사람이 별로 없네. = Wow, there are not very many people.

Transformative Endings

(1) -기

Used after a verb stem, -기 is an ending that transforms a verb into a noun.

Ex) 일어나다 = to get up / 일어나기 = getting up
일하다 = to work / 일하기 = working

(2) -(으)ㄴ, -는, -(으)ㄹ

Used after a verb stem, -(으)ㄴ, -는, or -(으)ㄹ transforms a verb into a modifying adjective that can be used in front of a noun.

Conjugations

Present Tense	Action Verbs	Verb stem (in this case, ㄹ is dropped when at the end of the verb stem) + -는 Ex) 좋아하다 = to like 좋아하는 = that I like, that likes
	Descriptive Verbs (= adjectives in infinitive form)	Verb stems ending with a vowel + -ㄴ Ex) 예쁘다 = to be pretty 예쁜 = pretty
		Verb stems ending with a consonant + -은 Ex) 좋다 = to be good 좋은 = good
		Verb stems ending with 있 or 없 + -는 Ex) 맛있다 = to be delicious 맛있는 = delicious

Past Tense	Action Verbs	Verb stems ending with a vowel or the consonant ㄹ (in which case ㄹ is dropped) + -ㄴ Ex) 가다 = to go 간 = where I went, that went Verb stems ending with a consonant (except for the consonant ㄹ) + -은 Ex) 먹다 = to eat 먹은 = that I ate, that ate
Future Tense	Action Verbs	Verb stems ending with a vowel or the consonant ㄹ (in which case ㄹ is dropped) + -ㄹ Ex) 그만두다 = to quit 그만둘 = that I will quit, that will quit
		Verb stems ending with a consonant (except for the consonant ㄹ) + -을 Ex) 웃다 = to smile 웃을 = that I will smile at, that will smile

Connective Endings

(1) -아/어/여서

Used after a verb stem, -아/어/여서 connects reason and result.

Ex) 안 느끼해서 맛있다. = It tastes good because it is not greasy.

(2) -(으)니까

Used after a verb stem, -(으)니까 connects reason and result.

Ex) 더우니까 수영장 가고 싶다. = I want to go to the swimming pool because it is hot.

(3) -(으)ㄴ/는데

Used after a verb stem, -(으)ㄴ/는데 connects a situation with a contrasting result.

Conjugations

Present Tense	Action Verbs	Verb stem + -는데 Ex) 나가야 되다 = to have to go out 나가야 되 + -는데 = 나가야 되는데 = I have to go out, but...
	Descriptive Verbs (= Adjectives in infinitive form)	Verb stems ending with a vowel or the consonant ㄹ (in which case ㄹ is dropped) + -ㄴ데 Ex) 예쁘다 = to be pretty 예쁘 + -ㄴ데 = 예쁜데 = it is pretty, but...
		Verb stems ending with a consonant (except for the consonant ㄹ) + -은데 Ex) 많다 = to be a lot 많 + -은데 = 많은데 = there are a lot, but...

	Nouns	Nouns + -인데 Ex) 주말 = weekend 주말인데 = it is the weekend, but...
Past Tense	Verbs	If the vowel of the last letter of the verb stem is ㅗ or ㅏ, attach -았는데. Ex) 들어오다 = to come in 들어오 + -았는데 = 들어왔는데 = I came in, but...
		If the vowel of the last letter of the verb stem is not ㅗ or ㅏ, attach -었는데. Ex) 넘어지다 = to fall down 넘어지 + -었는데 = 넘어졌는데 = I fell down, but...
		If the last letter of the verb stem is 하, attach -였는데. Ex) 하다 = to do 하 + -였는데 = 하였는데 = 했는데 = I did it, but... * 하였는데 is almost always shortened to 했는데.
	Nouns	Nouns ending with a consonant + -이었는데 Ex) 손님 = customer 손님 + -이었는데 = 손님이었는데 = I was a customer, but...

		Nouns ending with a vowel + -였는데 Ex) 카페 = cafe 카페 + -였는데 = 카페였는데 = it was a cafe, but...
Future Tense	Action Verbs	Verb stems ending with a vowel or the consonant ㄹ (in which case ㄹ is dropped) + -ㄹ 것인데 Ex) 일어나다 = to get up 일어나 + -ㄹ 건데 = 일어날 것인데 = 일어날 건데 = I am going to get up, but... * 것인데 is almost always shortened to 건데.
		Verb stems ending with a consonant (except for the consonant ㄹ) + -을 것인데 Ex) 받다 = to receive 받 + -을 것인데 = 받을 것인데 = 받을 건데 = I am going to receive it, but...

(4) -(으)면

Used after a verb stem, -(으)면 connects a condition with an expected result.

Ex) 미국으로 돌아가면 여기 다시 올 수 있을까?
= If I go back to the US, will I be able to come here again?

Particles

Subject Marking Particles: -이/가

Subject marking particles are placed after a noun to indicate that THAT noun is the subject of the sentence. If the noun ends with a consonant, it is followed by -이. If the noun ends with a vowel, it is followed by -가.

Ex) 점심시간이 즐겁다. = Lunchtime is enjoyable.
아빠가 좋아한다. = Dad likes it.

Topic Marking Particles: -은/는

Topic marking particles are placed after a noun to indicate that THAT noun is the topic of the sentence. If the noun ends with a consonant, it is followed by -은. If the noun ends with a vowel, it is followed by -는.

Ex) 케이크는 커피와 함께 먹어야 한다. = As for cake, you have to eat it with coffee.
운전은 처음 해 본다. = As for driving, I have never done it.

Object Marking Particles: -을/를

Object marking particles are placed after a noun to indicate that THAT noun is the direct object of the verb in the sentence. If the noun ends with a consonant, it is followed by -을. If the noun ends with a vowel, it is followed by -를.

Ex) 그림책을 샀다. = I bought a picture book.
영화를 봤다. = I watched a movie.

Adverbial Marking Particles

-에[1]	in, at, to (location) Ex) 백화점에 = in a department store, to a department store
-에[2]	at, during (time) Ex) 수업 시간에 = during class
-에[3]	in, per (criterion) Ex) 1년에 100권 = 100 books in a year
-에[4]	for (target) Ex) 몸에 좋다 = to be good for the body
-에서	in, at Ex) 카페에서 = at a cafe
-한테	to Ex) 다혜 씨한테 = to Dahye
-(으)로	to, toward Ex) 미국으로 = to the US
-(이)랑	with Ex) 엄마랑 = with Mom

-와/과	with Ex) 커피와 = with coffee
-보다	than Ex) 생각보다 = than I think

Adnominal Marking Particle: -의

Used after a noun, an adnominal marking particle changes the noun into a phrase that modifies that following noun.

(1) when the first noun is the time at which the following noun happens or is situated

Ex) 오늘의 점심 = today's lunch

(2) when the first noun is the person who made, achieved or possesses what the following noun refers to

Ex) 현우의 글씨 = Hyunwoo's handwriting

(3) when the first noun is the subject of a behavior or action that the following noun refers to

Ex) 언니의 졸업 = my sister's graduation

Auxiliary Particles

-부터	since, from Ex) 아침부터 = since morning
-까지	until, up to, by Ex) 오늘까지 = by today
-만	only Ex) 주말에만 = only on the weekend
-밖에	nothing but Ex) 이것밖에 = nothing but this
-들	plural suffix Ex) 사람들 = people
-도	also, too, as well Ex) 오늘도 = today as well

Expressions

Verb + -아/어/여야 하다	have to, must Ex) 회사에 가야 하다 = to have to go to work
Verb + -아/어/여야 되다	have to, must Ex) 숙제해야 되다 = to have to do homework
Verb + -아/어/여 주다	to VERB (for someone) Ex) 확인해 주다 = to check (for someone)
Verb + -고 있다	to be VERB-ing Ex) 가고 있다 = to be going
Verb + -(으)ㄹ 수 없다	cannot, to be unable to Ex) 그만둘 수 없다 = to be unable to quit

Conjugations of Irregular Verbs

Irregulars: ㅎ

If the descriptive verb stem ends with ㅎ and is followed by a conjugation that starts with a vowel, the ㅎ is dropped. If the conjugation starts with -아/어-, not only is ㅎ dropped, but -아/어- changes to -애/에-.

Ex) 파랗다 = to be blue

파랗 + -(으)ㄴ → 파라 + -ㄴ → 파란 = blue

파랗 + -아/어/여요 → 파라 + -아요 → 파라애요 → 파래요. = It is blue.

Irregulars: ㅂ

If the verb stem ends with ㅂ and is followed by a conjugation that starts with a vowel, the ㅂ changes to 우.

Ex) 덥다 = to be hot

덥 + -(으)니까 → 더 + 우 + -니까 → 더우니까 = because it is hot

덥 + -아/어/여요 → 더우 + -어요 → 더우어요 → 더워요. = It is hot.

Irregulars: 르

If the verb stem ends with 르 and is followed by a conjugation that starts with -아/어/여- or -았/었/였-, the 르 changes to ㄹ and is placed at the end of the previous vowel. One more ㄹ is needed before adding the verb conjugation ending.

Ex) 들르다 = to stop by

들르 + -아/어/여 주세요 → 들ㄹ + -어 주세요 → 들러 주세요. = Please stop by.

들르 + -아/어/여요 → 들ㄹ + -어요 → 들러요. = I stop by.

1 DAY

[N] 시작 / [N] begins

휴가 시작

vacation begins

Breakdown:

휴가
vacation

시작
start, beginning

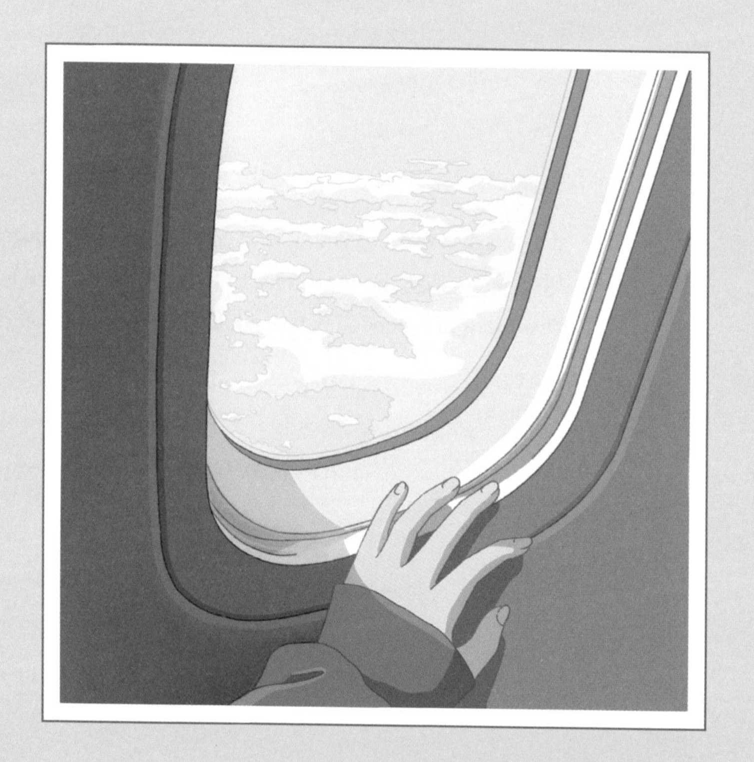

Listen to the audio track.

Write the Korean phrase here.

Do you want to post a picture on social media and let people know that you are beginning to do something? If so, you can just write the caption "[something] **시작**".

ex **회의 시작** *Write the phrase in Korean here.*

meeting begins

영화 시작

movie begins

You can also use "[something] **시작**" when you write your schedule down on your calendar.

ex

Mon	Tue	Wed	Thu	Fri
방학 시작 *school vacation begins*			운동 시작 *exercise begins*	

If you would like to add additional details about when something starts, you can use -**부터**, which means "from" or "since".

ex

오늘 = today 지금 = now 내일 = tomorrow 다음 주 = next week

오늘부터 휴가 시작

my vacation begins today

지금부터 회의 시작

the meeting begins now

내일부터 방학 시작

my school vacation starts tomorrow

다음 주부터 운동 시작

I will start exercising next week

If you would like to change the noun phrases above into complete sentences, you can use either 시작이다 or 시작한다.

오늘부터 휴가 시작이다. *Today is the start of vacation.*	오늘부터 휴가 시작한다. *My vacation starts today.*
지금부터 회의 시작이다. *It is now the beginning of the meeting.*	지금부터 회의 시작한다. *The meeting starts now.*

내일부터 방학 시작이다. *Tomorrow is the start of school vacation.*	내일부터 방학 시작한다. *School vacation starts tomorrow.*
다음 주부터 운동 시작이다. *Next week is the start of my exercise.*	다음 주부터 운동 시작한다. *I will start exercising next week.*

What are you going to start? When do you plan to begin?
Write your own story and share it with us on social media!

....

Words you might need: [N] 시작

N	
한국어 공부	studying Korean
요리	cooking
파티	party

2 DAY

[N1] + -(이)랑 [N2] / [N2] with [N1]

엄마랑 쇼핑

shopping with my mom

Breakdown:

엄마
mom

-(이)랑
with

쇼핑
shopping

 *Listen to the audio track.* .... 

Do you want to include what you did and who you did it with in your caption when you post a picture on social media? The simplest way to do this is to write "[someone] + -(이)랑 [something]".

ex 남자 친구랑 데이트

date with my boyfriend

조카랑 게임

game with my nephew/niece

"[someone] + -(이)랑 [something]" does not contain a verb, so it has no tense. Therefore, you can use it to talk about either what you plan to do or what you already did in the past.

ex

Mon	Tue	Wed	Thu	Fri
	동생이랑 영화 *movie with my younger brother/sister*			친구랑 공부 *studying with my friend*

Not only can you use this structure to talk about an activity, but you can also use it with a place name to talk about where you went.

ex 조카랑 놀이공원

theme park with my nephew/niece

친구랑 카페

cafe with my friend

You can also just write "[someone] -(이)랑" when you post a picture, especially when it is obvious what you did from the picture or when the activity itself is not important.

ex 엄마랑

with my mom

동생이랑

with my younger brother/sister

If you would like to write a complete sentence, you can add the appropriate verb in conjugated form to the object. If it's a journal entry, you will need to conjugate the verb using -았/었/였다, which is the past tense ending.

ex

엄마랑 쇼핑을 했다.
I went shopping with my mom.

동생이랑 영화를 봤다.
I watched a movie with my younger brother/sister.

조카랑 놀이공원에 갔다.
I went to a theme park with my nephew/niece.

If you would like to write what you did along with where you did it in one sentence, you can add -에서 to the location.

ex

엄마랑 쇼핑몰에서 쇼핑을 했다.
I went shopping with my mom at a shopping mall.

친구랑 카페에서 공부를 했다.
I studied with my friend at a cafe.

동생이랑 영화관에서 영화를 봤다.
I watched a movie with my younger brother/sister at a movie theater.

Now, write your own story and share it with us on social media!

Words you might need:

[N1] + -(이)랑 [N2]

N1		N2	
언니	older sister (used by women)	콘서트	concert
누나	older sister (used by men)	공원	park
오빠	older brother (used by women)	자전거	bike
형	older brother (used by men)	수다	talk, chat

[N] 중 / in the middle of [N]

산책 중

in the middle of a walk

Breakdown:

산책
walk, stroll

중
in the middle of

Listen to the audio track.

If you want to post about what you are doing at the moment, you can simply write "[something] 중".

ex

회의 중

in the middle of a meeting

수업 중

in the middle of a class

When using a verb, you need to add -는 중 to the verb stem.

ex

산책하다 = to take a walk　　회의하다 = to discuss, to have a meeting

수업을 듣다 = to take a class

산책하는 중

in the middle of taking a walk

회의하는 중

in the middle of having a meeting

수업(을) 듣는 중

in the middle of taking a class

You can also use 중 to talk about a certain period in time.

ex

학기 중 *during the semester*	
방학 중 *during school vacation*	

You can also emphasize that you are CURRENTLY doing a certain action by using words like 지금 (= now) or 요즘 (= these days).

ex

지금 산책 중

in the middle of a walk right now

지금 회의 중

in the middle of a meeting right now

요즘 방학 중

on vacation these days

요즘 한국어 수업 듣는 중

taking a Korean class these days

If you would like to write the phrases above in complete sentences, simply add -(이)다.

지금 산책 중이다.
I am now taking a walk.

지금 회의 중이다.
I am now in a meeting.

요즘 방학 중이다.
I am on school vacation these days.

요즘 한국어 수업 듣는 중이다.
I am taking a Korean class these days.

What are you doing right now or these days?
Write your own story and share it with us on social media!

Words you might need:

[N] 중

N	
다이어트	being on a diet
춤 연습	dance practice
식사	having a meal

오늘도 [N] / [N] today as usual

오늘도 운동

exercising today as usual

Breakdown:

오늘
today

-도
also, too

운동
exercise

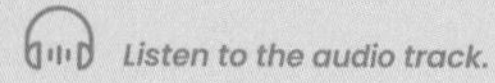
Listen to the audio track.

Do you go to the same coffee shop daily? Is there something you do regularly, almost every day? If so, this expression is perfect for you! When you post a picture of something you do or somewhere you go that is part of your usual routine, you can write the caption, "**오늘도** [something/somewhere]". It means "today as well" or "today as usual".

ex 오늘도 도서관

(at the) library today as usual

오늘도 마트

(at the) supermarket today as usual

You can also use the phrase "**오늘도** [something/somewhere]" when you write briefly about what you did that day in your weekly planner.

ex

Mon	Tue	Wed
오늘도 아르바이트 *Part-time job today as usual*		오늘도 산책! *Took a walk today as usual!*

You can use -부터 or -(이)랑, which were covered in Day 1 and Day 2, to add extra information about when you started or who you did something with.

ex

아침부터 = from morning　새벽부터 = from dawn　우리 강아지랑 = with my dog

오늘도 아침부터 운동

(I am) exercising in the morning today as usual

오늘도 새벽부터 도서관

(I am) at the library from dawn today as usual

오늘도 우리 강아지랑 산책

(I am) taking a walk with my dog today as usual

If you want to emphasize that you are in the middle of doing something, you can use 중 from Day 3.

ex 오늘도 아침부터 운동 중

in the middle of exercising from morning today as usual

오늘도 아르바이트 중

in the middle of working at my part-time job today as usual

오늘도 우리 강아지랑 산책 중

in the middle of walking with my dog today as usual

If you are writing a caption about something you already did or if you are writing in a journal at the end of the day, you can write a full sentence by using the appropriate verb in the past tense form.

ex

오늘도 아침부터 운동을 했다.
I exercised this morning today as well.

오늘도 새벽부터 도서관에 갔다.
I worked at my part-time job from dawn today as well.

오늘도 우리 강아지랑 산책을 했다.
I took a walk with my dog today as well.

DAY 4

If you are posting a picture of where you are at that moment, you can use the verb 오다.

ex

오늘도 도서관에 왔다.

I am here at the library today as usual.

오늘도 마트에 왔다.

I am here at a supermarket today as usual.

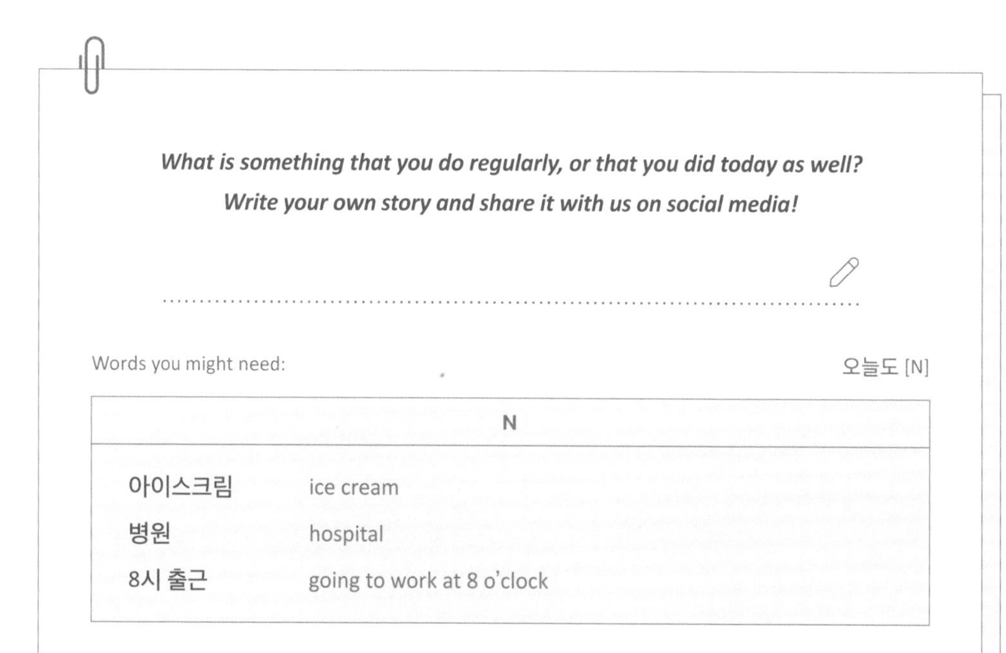

What is something that you do regularly, or that you did today as well?
Write your own story and share it with us on social media!

....

Words you might need:

오늘도 [N]

N	
아이스크림	ice cream
병원	hospital
8시 출근	going to work at 8 o'clock

[N] 전 / before [N]

외출 전

before going out

Breakdown:

외출
going out

전
before

Listen to the audio track.

Do you like posting pictures of yourself before going out to show off your outfit of the day? If so, this expression is perfect for you. You can use 전, which means "before", after the noun for the thing you are about to do, as in "[something] 전".

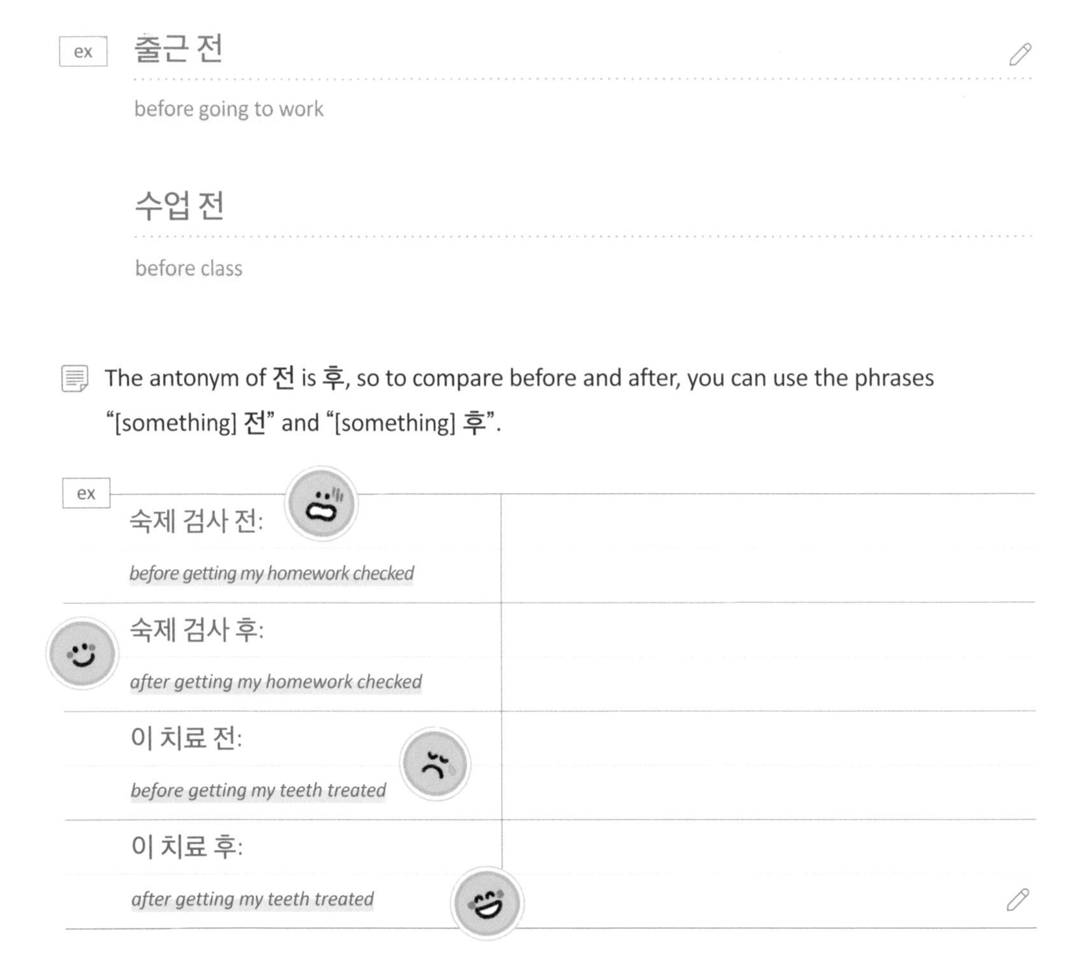

ex 출근 전

before going to work

수업 전

before class

The antonym of 전 is 후, so to compare before and after, you can use the phrases "[something] 전" and "[something] 후".

ex

숙제 검사 전:

before getting my homework checked

숙제 검사 후:

after getting my homework checked

이 치료 전:

before getting my teeth treated

이 치료 후:

after getting my teeth treated

To add [what you do] before [something], you can place another noun or noun group after "[something] 전".

ex

사진 한 장 = a picture 스페인어 공부 = studying Spanish 커피 한 잔 = a cup of coffee

외출 전 사진 한 장

a picture before going out

출근 전 스페인어 공부

studying Spanish before going to work

수업 전 커피 한 잔

a cup of coffee before class

If you would like to write the phrases above in complete sentences, you can add the appropriate verb in conjugated form after the object.

ex

외출 전 사진 한 장을 찍었다.

I took a picture before going out.

출근 전 스페인어 공부를 했다.
I studied Spanish before going to work.

수업 전 커피 한 잔을 마셨다.
I drank a cup of coffee before class.

Do you ever take a picture before doing something?
Write your own story and share it with us on social media!

Words you might need: [N] 전

N	
방 청소	cleaning a room
수술	surgery
출발	departure

6

DAY

[N1] + -이/가 좋아하는 [N2] / [N2] that [N1] likes

내가 좋아하는 옷

clothes that I like

Breakdown:

내
I (The original form is 나, which changes to 내 when used before the subject marking particle -이/가.)

-이/가
subject marking particle

좋아하다
to like

-(으)ㄴ/는
suffix that makes the previous word into a modifier

옷
clothes

 *Listen to the audio track.*

Do you want to share a picture of something you like with your followers? You can use the expression "**내가 좋아하는** [something]" when you share it.

ex 내가 좋아하는 카페

cafe that I like

내가 좋아하는 과자

snack that I like

When you want to talk about what someone else likes, you can use "[someone] + **-이/가 좋아하는** [something]".

ex

다혜가 좋아하는 노래 *song that Dahye likes*	
아빠가 좋아하는 TV 프로그램 *TV program that my dad likes*	

You can also add an adverb.

ex

제일 = most **요즘에** = these days **너무** = very, really

내가 제일 좋아하는 옷

my favorite clothes

다혜가 요즘에 좋아하는 노래

song that Dahye likes these days

아빠가 너무 좋아하는
TV 프로그램

TV program that my dad really likes

If you would like to change the noun phrases above into complete sentences, you can simply add -(이)다.

내가 제일 좋아하는 옷이다.
These are my favorite clothes.

다혜가 요즘에 좋아하는 노래다.
It is a song that Dahye likes these days.

아빠가 너무 좋아하는 TV 프로그램이다.
It is a TV program that my dad really likes.

What is something that you or someone you know likes?
Write your own story and share it with us on social media!

Words you might need:

[N1] + -이/가 좋아하는 [N2]

N1		N2	
우리 가족	my family	브랜드	brand
우리 회사 사람들	my coworkers	동네	neighborhood
우리 선생님	my teacher	식당	restaurant

[N] 끝 / [N] is done

청소 끝

cleaning is done

Breakdown:

청소
cleaning

끝
end, finish

Listen to the audio track.

DAY 7

Are you happy that something is over? If you want to post about it on social media, you can just write "[something] 끝".

ex 이사 끝

move is over

발표 끝

presentation is over

You can also use "[something] 끝" to mark the end of a certain period or event on your calendar.

ex

Mon	Tue	Wed	Thu	Fri
	시험 끝 *exams end*			학기 끝 *semester ends*

If you would like to express and emphasize the fact that you are happy that something is over, you can just add 드디어, which means "finally", and an exclamation mark.

ex 드디어 청소 끝!

Finally, cleaning is done!

드디어 이사 끝!

Finally, the move is over!

드디어 발표 끝!

Finally, the presentation is over!

드디어 시험 끝!

Finally, exams are over!

드디어 학기 끝!

Finally, the semester is over!

If you would like to write the phrases above in complete sentences, you can add either -이다 or use the verb 끝나다 in its past tense form, 끝났다.

드디어 청소 끝이다! *Finally, it is the end of cleaning!*	드디어 청소 끝났다! *Finally, I'm done with cleaning!*
드디어 이사 끝이다! *Finally, it is the end of moving!*	드디어 이사 끝났다! *Finally, I'm done with moving!*
드디어 발표 끝이다! *Finally, it is the end of the presentation!*	드디어 발표 끝났다! *Finally, the presentation is done!*
드디어 시험 끝이다! *Finally, it is the end of the exam!*	드디어 시험 끝났다! *Finally, the exam is over!*
드디어 학기 끝이다! *Finally, it is the end of the semester!*	드디어 학기 끝났다! *Finally, the semester is over!*

What is something that you have finished?

Write your own story and share it with us on social media!

Words you might need:

[N] 끝

N	
여행 준비	preparation for a trip
과제	assignment
축제	festival

DAY 1.

[N] 시작

DAY 2.

[N1] + -(이)랑 [N2]

DAY 5.

[N] 전

DAY 6.

[N1] + -이/가 좋아하는 [N2]

앞에서 배운 패턴을 사용해, 다이어리의 위클리 페이지를 채워 보세요!

Fill in the weekly review page using the patterns you previously learned!

DAY 3. [N] 중	DAY 4. 오늘도 [N]
DAY 7. [N] 끝	

8

DAY

오랜만에 [N] / [N] for the first time in a while

오랜만에 치킨

fried chicken for the first time in a while

Breakdown:

오랜만
after a long time

-에
time marking particle

치킨
fried chicken

 *Listen to the audio track.*

If you want to post a picture of something you did for the first time in a while, the shortest caption you can write is "**오랜만에** [something]".

ex 오랜만에 가족사진

family picture for the first time in a while

오랜만에 원피스

first time in a while wearing a dress

You can also write "**오랜만에** [something]" in your weekly planner to talk about either what you did or what you will do for the first time in a while.

ex

Fri	Sat	Sun
오랜만에 홍대 *Hongdae for the first time in a while*		오랜만에 영화관 *movie theater for the first time in a while*

To express what you did more specifically, you can add an appropriate verb conjugated with -(으)ㄴ, which turns the verb into a modifier.

ex

먹다 = to eat　찍다 = to take　입다 = to wear, to put on　가다 = to go

오랜만에 먹은 치킨

fried chicken that I ate for the first time in a while

오랜만에 찍은 가족사진

family picture that we took for the first time in a while

오랜만에 입은 원피스

dress that I put on for the first time in a while

오랜만에 간 홍대

Hongdae, where I went for the first time in a while

오랜만에 간 영화관

movie theater, where I went for the first time in a while

If you would like to write the phrases above in complete sentences, swap the position of the verb and the object, and then add the object marking particle -을/를.

ex

오랜만에 치킨을 먹었다.
I ate fried chicken for the first time in a while.

오랜만에 가족사진을 찍었다.
We took a family picture for the first time in a while.

오랜만에 원피스를 입었다.
I put on a dress for the first time in a while.

To talk about a place you visited for the first time in a while, add the location marking particle -에.

ex

오랜만에 홍대에 갔다.
I went to Hongdae for the first time in a while.

오랜만에 영화관에 갔다.
I went to a movie theater for the first time in a while.

What have you done recently for the first time in a while?
Write your own story and share it with us on social media!

Words you might need:

오랜만에 [N]

N	
학교	school
외식	eating out
외출	going out

9

DAY

너무 [Adj] + -다! / It is so [Adj]!

너무 귀엽다!

It is so cute!

Breakdown:

너무
too, so

귀엽다
to be cute

 *Listen to the audio track.*

Have you just seen something that is really cute or funny and do you want to post about it on social media? Here's how to make an exclamatory sentence to express yourself. You can write "너무 [the adjective to describe how it is] + -다!"

ex 너무 예쁘다!

It is so pretty!

너무 맛있다!

It is so yummy!

The exclamation mark is not always necessary. If your intended tone is calm, you can just use a period.

ex

너무 힘들다. *It is so tough.*	
너무 재밌다. *It is so enjoyable.*	

If your sentence includes a subject, you can add it before 너무.

ex

이 고양이 = this cat
이 목걸이 = this necklace
이 파스타 = this pasta
회사 일 = work (in an office)

이 고양이 너무 귀엽다!

This cat is so cute!

이 목걸이 너무 예쁘다!

This necklace is so pretty!

이 파스타 너무 맛있다!

This pasta is so yummy!

회사 일이 너무 힘들다.

Work (at my office) is so tiring.

회사 일이 너무 재밌다.

Work (at my office) is so enjoyable.

You can also use -아/어/여서 to add a reason.

ex

통통하다 = to be chubby　　느끼하다 = to be greasy, to be rich　　많다 = to be a lot

이 고양이 통통해서

너무 귀엽다!

This cat is so cute because it is chubby!

이 파스타 안 느끼해서

너무 맛있다!

This pasta is so yummy because it is not too rich!

회사 일이 많아서

너무 힘들다.

I am so tired because I have a lot of work (at my office).

What is something that has left an impression on you?
Write your own story and share it with us on social media!

Words you might need:

너무 [Adj] + -다!

Adj	
비싸다	to be expensive
작다	to be small
깨끗하다	to be clean

[N1] + -의 [N2] Part 1 / [N1]'s [N2] Part 1

오늘의 점심

today's lunch

Breakdown:

오늘
today

-의
's, of

점심
lunch

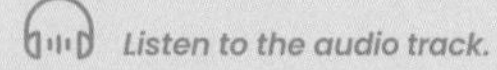

When you post a picture of something relevant to a certain period of time, you might want to write something like, "today's [something]" or "this year's [something]". In Korean, you can write "[certain period] + -의 [something/someone]".

ex 오늘의 하늘

today's sky

어제의 나

me yesterday

You can also use the phrase "[certain period] + -의 [something]" when you write in your journal.

ex

올해의 목표 *this year's goal*	
2월 1일의 일기 *February 1 diary entry*	

When you use "[certain period] + -의 [something]", you can modify "[something]" with an adjective, which is placed before "[something]". A descriptive verb can be made into an adjective by adding -(으)ㄴ/는 to the verb stem (see p. 21).

ex

맛있다 = to be yummy　　파랗다 = to be blue　　머리(가) 길다 = to have long hair

오늘의 맛있는 점심

today's yummy lunch

오늘의 파란 하늘

today's blue sky

어제의 머리 긴 나

yesterday's me with long hair

If you would like to modify the entire phrase "[certain period] + -의 [something]" with an adjective or an adjective phrase, you can place the adjective before "[certain period] + -의 [something]".

ex

내가 세우다 = I set (something)　　딸이 쓰다 = daughter writes

내가 세운 올해의 목표

the goal I set for this year

딸이 쓴 2월 1일의 일기

February 1 diary entry that my daughter wrote

If you would like to write the phrases above in complete sentences, you need to conjugate the verb with -았/었/였다, which is the past tense ending.

ex

오늘의 점심은 정말 맛있었다.
Today's lunch was really yummy.

오늘의 하늘은 정말 파랬다.
Today's sky was really blue.

어제의 나는 머리가 길었다.
Yesterday's me had long hair.

Is there a moment that you want to share?
Write your own story and share it with us on social media!

....

Words you might need:

[N1] + -의 [N2]

N1		N2	
1999년	the year 1999	서울	Seoul
작년 여름	last summer	우리 가족	my family
지난 주말	last weekend	날씨	weather

[N1] + -의 [N2] Part 2 / [N1]'s [N2] Part 2

예지의 그림

Yeji's drawing

Breakdown:

예지
Yeji (name of a person)

-의
's, of

그림
drawing, picture

Listen to the audio track.

If you want to post a picture of something that belongs to or was done by someone else, you can just write "[someone] + -의 [something]".

ex 아빠의 문자 메시지

my dad's text message

현우의 글씨

Hyunwoo's handwriting

You can, of course, elaborate by using an appropriate verb conjugated with -(으)ㄴ/는.

ex

그리다 = to draw 보내다 = to send 쓰다 = to write

예지가 그린 그림 

drawing that Yeji drew

아빠가 보낸 문자 메시지

text message that Dad sent

현우가 쓴 글씨

handwritten message that Hyunwoo wrote

You can also use "[someone]'s [something]" when you write events down on your calendar, but in this case, it is more natural to omit -의.

ex

Mon	Tue	Wed	Thu	Fri
동생(의) 생일 *my younger brother / sister's birthday*			언니(의) 졸업 *my older sister's graduation*	

If you add additional information to show what kind of event it is, however, -의 is not usually omitted.

ex

스무 번째 = 20th　　대학교 = university　　웃기다 = to be funny
따뜻하다 = to be warm　　못생기다 = to be ugly

동생의 스무 번째 생일

my younger brother/sister's 20th birthday

언니의 대학교 졸업

my older sister's university graduation

예지의 웃긴 그림

Yeji's funny drawing

아빠의 따뜻한 문자 메시지

my dad's warm text message

현우의 못생긴 글씨

Hyunwoo's ugly handwriting

If you would like to write the phrases above in complete sentences, simply add -(이)다.

ex

동생의 스무 번째 생일이다.
It is my younger brother/sister's 20th birthday.

예지의 웃긴 그림이다.
It is Yeji's funny drawing.

아빠의 따뜻한 문자 메시지다.
It is my dad's warm text message.

Now, write your own story and share it with us on social media!

Words you might need:

[N1] + -의 [N2]

N1	N2	
You can use any name here.	표정	facial expression
	편지	letter
	손	hand

[N] + -을/를 [V] + -았/었/였다. / I [V] [N].

카메라를 샀다.

I bought a camera.

Breakdown:

카메라
camera

-을/를
object marking particle

사다
to buy

-았/었/였-
past tense suffix

-다
past tense verb ending

 *Listen to the audio track.*

Sometimes you have nothing special to write about the picture you're going to post. You just want to write a simple sentence that delivers a fact. When that's the case, "[something/someone] + -을/를 [what you do] + -았/었/였다" is the structure for you.

ex 다혜를 만났다.

I met Dahye.

연극을 봤다.

I watched a play.

You can also use the same structure to briefly write about what you did that day in your weekly planner.

ex

Fri	Sat	Sun
	아르바이트를 시작했다. *I started a part-time job.*	친구 결혼식에 갔다. *I went to my friend's wedding.*

To explain more about [something/someone], you can add an adjective or an adjective phrase in front of it. Descriptive verbs can be made into adjectives by adding -(으)ㄴ/는 to the verb stem.

ex

오래되다 = to be old

학교에 가고 있다 = to be on one's way to school

재밌다 = to be fun

주말에만 하다 = to do only on the weekend

부산에서 하다 = to be held in Busan

오래된 카메라를 샀다.

I bought an old camera.

학교에 가고 있는

다혜를 만났다.

I bumped into Dahye who was on her way to school.

재밌는 연극을 봤다.

I watched a fun play.

주말에만 하는

아르바이트를 시작했다.

I started a part-time job that I only do on the weekends.

부산에서 하는

친구 결혼식에 갔다.

I went to my friend's wedding that was held in Busan.

What did you do today?

Write your own story and share it with us on social media!

Words you might need:

[N] + -을/를 [V] + -았/었/였다.

N		V	
빵	bread	만들다	to make
신발	shoes	버리다	to throw away
책상	desk	바꾸다	to change

13

DAY

아! [V] + -고 싶다! / Ah! I want to [V]!

아! 여행 가고 싶다!

Ah! I want to travel!

Breakdown:

아!
Ah!

여행
travel, trip

가다
to go

-고 싶다
to want to

 *Listen to the audio track.*

Sometimes you post a picture of something you want to do or somewhere you want to go. In this type of situation, you can write "[what you do] + -고 싶다!" If you want to emphasize that you really want to do it, you can add "아!" at the beginning.

ex 아! 옷 사고 싶다!

Ah! I want to buy clothes!

아! 수영장 가고 싶다!

Ah! I want to go to the swimming pool!

You can also use this sentence structure when writing in a journal.

ex

아! 가족들 보고 싶다! *(lit.) Ah! I want to see my family!*	
아! 한국어 잘하고 싶다! *Ah! I want to be good at Korean!*	

To mention what made you feel that way, you can use -(으)니까, which means "since" or "because".

ex

바다 사진(을) 보다 = to look at a photo of the ocean

예쁜 옷(을) 보다 = to look at pretty clothes

너무 덥다 = to be too hot

가족들이랑 통화하다 = to talk to one's family members over the phone

한국어 잘하는 사람(을) 보다 = to see someone who is good at Korean

바다 사진 보니까

여행 가고 싶다!

Since I'm looking at a photo of the ocean, I want to travel!

예쁜 옷 보니까

옷 사고 싶다!

Since I'm looking at pretty clothes, I want to buy clothes!

너무 더우니까

수영장 가고 싶다!

Since it's too hot, I want to go to the swimming pool!

가족들이랑 통화하니까

가족들 보고 싶다!

Since I talked to my family members on the phone, I want to see them!

한국어 잘하는 사람 보니까

나도 한국어 잘하고 싶다!

Since I saw someone who is good at Korean, I want to be good at Korean as well!

You can also use -고 싶어지다, which is a combination of -고 싶다 and -아/어/여지다 (= to become), to emphasize that something changed your state and made you want to do something or go somewhere.

ex 바다 사진 보니까

여행 가고 싶어졌다.

Looking at a photo of the ocean made me want to travel.

예쁜 옷 보니까

옷 사고 싶어졌다.

Looking at pretty clothes made me want to buy clothes.

너무 더우니까

수영장 가고 싶어졌다.

Extremely hot weather made me want to go to the swimming pool.

가족들이랑 통화하니까

가족들 보고 싶어졌다.

Talking to my family members on the phone made me want to see them.

한국어 잘하는 사람 보니까

나도 한국어 잘하고 싶어졌다.

Seeing at someone who is good at Korean made me want to be good at Korean as well.

What is something that you want to do?
Is there something that made you crave something?
Write your own story and share it with us on social media!

Words you might need:

아! [V] + -고 싶다!

V	
놀다	to hang out, to not work
자다	to sleep
나가다	to go out

14 DAY

아! [V] + -기 싫다! / Ugh! I don't want to [V]!

아! 일어나기 싫다!

Ugh! I don't want to get up!

Breakdown:

아!
Ugh!

일어나다
to get up

-기 싫다
do not want to

Listen to the audio track.

Aren't there moments when you don't want to do something even though you do it every day? If you want to share those moments on social media, you just need to remember the expression "아! [what you do] + -기 싫다!"

ex

아! 나가기 싫다!

Ugh! I don't want to go out!

아! 일하기 싫다!

Ugh! I don't want to go to work!

You can also use this sentence structure when writing in a journal.

ex

아! 숙제하기 싫다! *Ugh! I don't want to do my homework!*	
아! 학교 가기 싫다! *Ugh! I don't want to go to school!*	

To mention what made you feel that way, you can use -(으)니까.

ex

피곤하다 = to be tired   비가 오다 = to rain   날씨가 좋다 = the weather is good

아! 피곤하니까 일어나기 싫다!

Ugh! Since I'm tired, I don't want to get up!

비가 오니까 나가기 싫다!

Since it's raining, I don't want to go out!

날씨가 좋으니까 일하기 싫다!

Since the weather is good, I don't want to work!

If you would like to add "even though I have to do it" to the sentence, you can use -아/어/어야 되는데.

ex 아! 나가야 되는데,

나가기 싫다! 

Ugh! I have to go out, but I don't want to!

아! 숙제해야 되는데,

숙제하기 싫다!

Ugh! I have to do my homework, but I don't want to!

아! 학교 가야 되는데,

학교 가기 싫다!

Ugh! I have to go to school, but I don't want to!

What is something that you hate doing or don't want to do?
Write your own story and share it with us on social media!

Words you might need:

아! [V] + -기 싫다!

V			
움직이다	to move	요리하다	to cook
노래하다	to sing		

[V] + -기 성공 / success in [V] + -ing

1년에 책 100권 읽기 성공

success in reading 100 books in a year

Breakdown:

년
year

-에
in

책
book

권
counter for books

읽다
to read

-기
suffix that changes verbs into nouns

성공
success

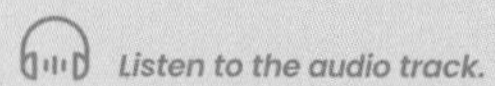
Listen to the audio track.

Have you succeeded in doing something and do you want to boast about it on social media? To do so, you can simply write "[what you have succeeded in] + -기 성공". Simply attach -기 to the end of the verb stem.

ex 일찍 일어나기 성공

success in getting up early

강아지랑 사진 찍기 성공

success in taking a photo with the puppy

At the end of each day, you can use this expression to write about what you successfully did that day in your journal.

ex

Mon	Tue	Wed
다혜 씨한테 말 걸기 성공 *success in talking to Dahye*		오늘은 일찍 퇴근하기 성공 *success in leaving work early today*

If "[what you have succeeded at]" is expressed as a verb, you must conjugate it with -기 as shown above. However, if it can be expressed as a noun, you don't need to attach -기. You can just say "[what you have succeeded at] 성공".

ex 겨울 코트 쇼핑 성공 

success in winter coat shopping

5kg 다이어트 성공

success in losing 5 kg

If you would like to write the phrases above in complete sentences, you can use the verb form of 성공, which is 성공하다, in the past tense.

1년에 책 100권 읽기 성공했다.
I succeeded in reading 100 books in a year.

일찍 일어나기 성공했다.
I succeeded in getting up early.

강아지랑 사진 찍기 성공했다.
I succeeded in taking a photo with the puppy.

다혜 씨한테 말 걸기 성공했다.
I succeeded in talking to Dahye.

오늘은 일찍 퇴근하기 성공했다.
I succeeded in leaving work early today.

겨울 코트 쇼핑 성공했다.
I succeeded in winter coat shopping.

5kg 다이어트 성공했다.
I succeeded in losing 5 kg.

What have you succeeded in?
Write your own story and share it with us on social media!

Words you might need:

[V] + -기 성공

V	
일찍 출근하다	to go to work early
게임 하루에 한 시간만 하다	to play games only for an hour a day
친구 몰래 파티 준비하다	to plan a party without my friend finding out

Weekly: Review

DAY 8. 오랜만에 [N]	DAY 9. 너무 [Adj] + -다!
DAY 12. [N] + -을/를 [V] + -았/었/였다.	DAY 13. 아! [V] + -고 싶다!

앞에서 배운 패턴을 사용해, 다이어리의 위클리 페이지를 채워 보세요!

Fill in the weekly review page using the patterns you previously learned!

DAY 10.

[N1] + -의 [N2]

DAY 11.

[N1] + -의 [N2]

DAY 14.

아! [V] + -기 싫다!

DAY 15.

[V] + -기 성공

16 DAY

나를 위한 [N] / [N] for me

나를 위한 선물

a present for myself

Breakdown:

나
I, me

-을/를
object marking particle

위하다
to be for

-(으)ㄴ/는
suffix that turns the previous word into a modifier

선물
present, gift

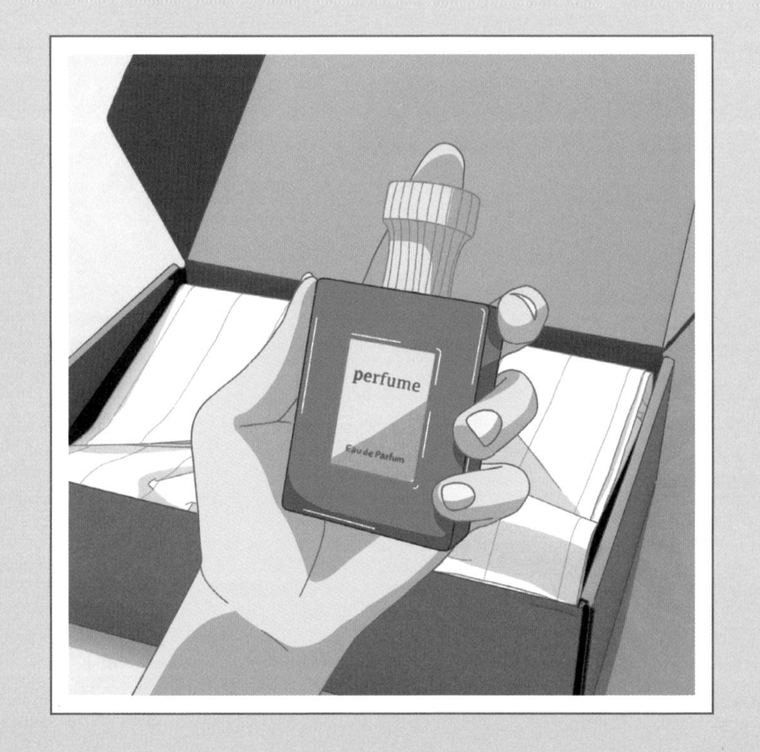

 *Listen to the audio track.*

Do you often do something just for yourself? If you buy something for yourself, it can be referred to as a "gift for yourself", and if you spend time by yourself, it can be referred to as "time for yourself". In Korean, you can express this as "**나를 위한** [something]".

ex 나를 위한 시간

time for myself

나를 위한 그림책

picture book for myself

You can also use "**나를 위한** [something]" to briefly describe your day on your calendar.

ex

Mon	Tue	Wed	Thu	Fri
	나를 위한 선택 *a choice I made for myself*		나를 위한 하루 *a day for myself*	

Of course, you can also replace 나 with someone else.

ex 아이들을 위한 파티

party for children

남편을 위한 노래

song for my husband

아내를 위한 요리

dish for my wife

To write the phrases above in complete sentences, add the appropriate verb in conjugated form after [N].

ex

나를 위한 그림책을 샀다.
I bought a picture book for myself.

나를 위한 선택을 했다.
I made a choice for myself.

나를 위한 하루를 보냈다.
I spent the day for myself.

아이들을 위한 파티를 열었다.
I held a party for my children.

What is something that you have done for yourself?
Write your own story and share it with us on social media!

Words you might need: 나를 위한 [N]

N	
여행	travel
꽃	flower
추천	recommendation

[N1] + -은/는 [N2] + -와/과 함께 / [N1] goes well with [N2]

케이크는 커피와 함께

cake goes well with coffee

Breakdown:

케이크
cake

-은/는
topic marking particle

커피
coffee

-와/과
with

함께
together

 *Listen to the audio track.*

Are there any food pairings that you eat often? If you want to post about them on social media, all you have to write is "[food] + -은/는 [food] + -와/과 함께".

ex 햄버거는 콜라와 함께

hamburgers go well with cola

베이글은 크림치즈와 함께

bagels go well with cream cheese

If you add the adverb 역시, which means "as expected" or "indeed", you can emphasize the fact that you think the pairing is just as good as you expected.

ex 케이크는 역시 커피와 함께

cake goes well with coffee indeed

햄버거는 역시 콜라와 함께

hamburgers go well with cola indeed

베이글은 역시 크림치즈와 함께

bagels go well with cream cheese indeed

People often use the expression "[food] + -에는 역시 [food]" as well. -에는 means "as for" or "to" in this case, and the whole structure has the same meaning as "[food] + -은/는 [food] + -와/과 함께".

ex 케이크에는 역시 커피

cake and, of course, coffee

햄버거에는 역시 콜라

hamburgers and, of course, cola

베이글에는 역시 크림치즈

bagels with, of course, cream cheese

You can also use this structure in your weekly planner. "[Food] + -에는 역시 [food]" means that the first food must indeed be eaten together with the second food or beverage.

ex

Mon	Tue	Wed
오늘의 아침: 빵, 오렌지 주스 *today's breakfast: bread, orange juice* 빵에는 역시 오렌지 주스 *bread and, of course, orange juice*	오늘의 저녁: 라면, 김치 *today's dinner: ramyeon, kimchi* 라면에는 역시 김치 *ramyeon and, of course, kimchi*	

If you would like to write the phrases above in complete sentences, simply add -(이)다.

케이크에는 역시 커피다.
It's cake and, of course, coffee.

햄버거에는 역시 콜라다.
It's hamburgers and, of course, cola.

베이글에는 역시 크림치즈다.
It's bagels with, of course, cream cheese.

빵에는 역시 오렌지 주스다.
It's bread and, of course, orange juice.

라면에는 역시 김치다.
It's ramyeon and, of course, kimchi.

Are there any food pairings that you like?
Write your own story and share it with us on social media!

Words you might need:

[N1] + -은/는 [N2] + -와/과 함께

N1 / N2			
도넛	doughnut	프렌치프라이	french fries
우유	milk	연어	salmon

[N] + -은/는 처음 / first time [N]

운전은 처음

first time driving

Breakdown:

운전
driving

-은/는
topic marking particle

처음
first

 *Listen to the audio track.*

Would you like to share a moment when you tried something for the first time? If so, the simplest phrase you can use is "[something] +-은/는 처음".

ex 제주도는 처음

first time on Jeju Island

비행기는 처음

first time on an airplane

Another way to write about a new experience you just had is "처음 [what you have done for the first time] + -아/어/여 본 [something]". -아/어/여 보다 means "to try doing something".

ex

하다 = to do 오다 = to come 타다 = to get on, to take

처음 해 본 운전

tried driving for the first time

처음 와 본 제주도

came to Jeju Island for the first time

처음 타 본 비행기

took an airplane for the first time

You can also use the phrase "처음 [what you have done for the first time] + -아/어/여 본 [something]" when you write in your weekly planner.

ex

Fri	Sat	Sun
처음 먹어 본 한국 음식 *tried Korean food for the first time*		처음 가 본 콘서트 *went to a concert for the first time*

If you would like to write the phrases above in complete sentences, you can simply conjugate -아/어/여 보다 into the past tense.

운전을 처음 해 봤다.
I drove for the first time.

제주도를 처음 와 봤다.
I came to Jeju Island for the first time.

비행기를 처음 타 봤다.
I flew on an airplane for the first time.

한국 음식을 처음 먹어 봤다.
I tried Korean food for the first time.

콘서트를 처음 가 봤다.
I went to a concert for the first time.

Is there anything that you tried for the first time recently?
Write your own story and share it with us on social media!

Words you might need:

[N] + -은/는 처음

N	
하이힐	high-heeled shoes
아르바이트	part-time job
등산	hiking

[V] + -(으)ㄹ 때 [Adj] + -(으)ㄴ/는 [N]
/ [N] who is [Adj] when they [V]

웃을 때 예쁜 소희

Sohee who is pretty when she smiles

Breakdown:

웃다
to smile, to laugh

-(으)ㄹ 때
when

예쁘다
to be pretty

-(으)ㄴ/는
suffix that turns the previous word into a modifier

소희
Sohee (name of a person)

 *Listen to the audio track.*

When you post a photo of someone on social media, you can describe their characteristics or features more specifically by using the structure, "[what the person in the photo does] + -(으)ㄹ 때 [the adjective to describe how they are] + -(으)ㄴ/는 [someone]".

ex 먹을 때 조용한 다혜

Dahye who is quiet when she eats

운전할 때 멋있는 경화

Kyung-hwa who looks cool when she drives

You can use this structure in a variety of ways including on social media, in text messages, and in your journal. It works to describe just about any picture of a person. Here are some more examples.

ex

화낼 때 귀여운 현우 *Hyunwoo who looks cute when he gets angry*	
노래할 때 멋있는 경은 *Kyeong-eun who looks cool when she sings*	

People often add **제일**, which means “the most”, for emphasis.

웃을 때 제일 예쁜 소희

Sohee who is prettiest when she smiles

먹을 때 제일 조용한 다혜

Dahye who is quietest when she eats

운전할 때 제일 멋있는 경화

Kyunghwa who looks coolest when she drives

화낼 때 제일 귀여운 현우

Hyunwoo who looks cutest when he gets angry

노래할 때 제일 멋있는 경은

Kyeong-eun who looks coolest when she sings

Of course, you can also use this phrase to describe yourself.

ex 먹을 때 제일 조용한 나

me who is quietest when eating

운전할 때 제일 멋있는 나

me who looks coolest when driving

If you would like to write the phrases above in complete sentences, you can just add -(이)다.

ex

운을 때 제일 예쁜 소희다.
It is Sohee, who is prettiest when she smiles.

노래할 때 제일 멋있는 경은이다.
It is Kyeong-eun, who looks coolest when she sings.

먹을 때 제일 조용한 나다.
It is me, who is quietest when eating.

You can also change the word order so the person's name becomes the subject and the adjective becomes the predicate of the sentence.

ex

소희는 웃을 때 제일 예쁘다.
Sohee is prettiest when she smiles.

경은이는 노래할 때 제일 멋있다.
Kyeong-eun looks coolest when she sings.

나는 먹을 때 제일 조용하다.
I am quietest when eating.

Is there anyone you want to describe?
Write your own story and share it with us on social media!

....

Words you might need:

[V] + -(으)ㄹ 때 [Adj] + -(으)ㄴ/는 [N]

V		Adj	
일하다	to work	똑똑하다	to be smart
춤추다	to dance	행복해 보이다	to look happy
배고프다	to be hungry	부지런하다	to be diligent

20

DAY

[Adj] + -(으)ㄴ/는 [N] / [Adj] [N]

피곤한 월요일

tiring Monday

Breakdown:

피곤하다
to be tired, to be tiring

-(으)ㄴ/는
suffix that turns the previous word into a modifier

월요일
Monday

 *Listen to the audio track.*

Having a great day? Enjoying a pleasant morning? You can describe what kind of day or time you are having by using the noun phrase "[how something is] + -(으)ㄴ/는 [something]".

ex 즐거운 점심시간

happy lunchtime

기분 좋은 아침

pleasant morning

You can also summarize your day using "[how something is] + -(으)ㄴ/는 [something]" in your weekly planner.

ex

Wed	Thu	Fri
제일 힘든 수요일 *the toughest Wednesday*		제일 바쁜 금요일 *the busiest Friday*

You can use -아/어/여서, which means "because" or "so", to add a reason.

ex

오랜만에 출근하다 = to go to work after a long time away

맛있는 거 먹다 = to eat something good

일찍 일어나다 = to get up early

한 주의 중간에 있다 = to be in the middle of a week

회의가 많다 = there are a lot of meetings

오랜만에 출근해서

피곤한 월요일

I'm tired on Mondays from coming back to work after a long time away

맛있는 거 먹어서

즐거운 점심시간

lunchtime is enjoyable because I eat something good

일찍 일어나서

기분 좋은 아침

I got up early so I feel good this morning

한 주의 중간에 있어서

제일 힘든 수요일

Wednesdays are the toughest because they're in the middle of the week

회의가 많아서

제일 바쁜 금요일

I'm the busiest on Fridays because I have a lot of meetings

If you would like to write the phrases above in complete sentences, simply add -(이)다.

ex

오랜만에 출근해서 피곤한 월요일이다.
It is a tiring Monday because I came back to work after a long time away.

맛있는 거 먹어서 즐거운 점심시간이다.
It is an enjoyable lunchtime because I am eating something good.

일찍 일어나서 기분 좋은 아침이다.
It is a pleasant morning because I got up early.

You can also change the word order from 즐거운 점심시간이다 to 점심시간이 즐겁다. Both mean the same thing. Here are some examples.

ex

맛있는 거 먹어서 점심시간이 즐겁다.
I enjoy lunchtime because I eat something good.

한 주의 중간에 있어서 수요일이 제일 힘들다.
Wednesdays are the toughest because they're in the middle of the week.

회의가 많아서 금요일이 제일 바쁘다.
I am the busiest on Friday because I have a lot of meetings.

How would you describe your day?
Write your own story and share it with us on social media!

Words you might need:

[Adj] + -(으)ㄴ/는 [N]

Adj		N	
재미있다	to be fun	저녁 시간	evening, dinner time
시끄럽다	to be noisy	하루	day
지루하다	to be boring	사무실	office

[Adj] + -(으)ㄹ 것 같다. / I think it will be [Adj].

맛있을 것 같다.

I think it will be delicious.

Breakdown:

맛있다
to be delicious

-(으)ㄹ 것 같다
I think it will be

 *Listen to the audio track.*

Do you ever post a picture on social media when you find something that looks delicious or fun? If you want to write about an assumption you have, you can use the phrase "[how you think it will be] + -(으)ㄹ 것 같다".

ex 불편할 것 같다.

I think it will be inconvenient.

비쌀 것 같다.

I think it will be expensive.

You can also use "[how you think it will be] + -(으)ㄹ 것 같다" when making assumptions about something in your journal.

ex	
내일 추울 것 같다. *I think it will be cold tomorrow.*	
이번 시험 어려울 것 같다. *I think this exam will be difficult.*	

On social media, your followers will be able to tell what you are talking about by looking at your picture. However, if you want to add more specific information, you can include [what you are talking about] at the beginning of your sentence.

ex

이 피자 = this pizza　　이 의자 = this chair　　이 식당 = this restaurant

이 피자 맛있을 것 같다.

I think this pizza will be delicious.

이 의자 불편할 것 같다.

I think this chair will be uncomfortable.

이 식당 비쌀 것 같다.

I think this restaurant will be expensive.

You can also use -아/어/여서 to add the reason for your assumption.

ex

새우가 많이 올라가다 = a lot of shrimp is on it

너무 작다 = to be too small

백화점에 있다 = to be in a department store

비 오다 = to rain

선현우 교수님이 내다 = Professor Hyunwoo Sun makes (an exam)

이 피자 새우가 많이 올라가서

맛있을 것 같다.

Since there is a lot of shrimp on this pizza, I think it will be delicious.

이 의자 너무 작아서

불편할 것 같다.

Since this chair is too small, I think it will be uncomfortable.

이 식당 백화점에 있어서

비쌀 것 같다.

Since this restaurant is in a department store, I think it will be expensive.

내일 비 와서

추울 것 같다.

Since it will rain tomorrow, I think it will be cold.

이번 시험 문제 선현우 교수님이

내서 어려울 것 같다.

Since Professor Hyunwoo Sun made this exam, I think it will be difficult.

Do you have any assumptions that you want to share with your followers?
Write your own story and share it with us on social media!

....

Words you might need:

[Adj] + -(으)ㄹ 것 같다.

Adj	
답답하다	to be frustrated, to be frustrating, to be stuffy
괜찮다	to be all right, to be okay
무섭다	to be scary

22

DAY

[N] + -을/를 [V] + -(으)ㄹ까 고민 중
/ thinking about [V] + -ing [N]

머리를 자를까 고민 중

thinking about getting my hair cut

Breakdown:

머리
hair

-을/를
object marking particle

자르다
to cut

-(으)ㄹ까
if, whether

고민
thinking, debating

중
in the middle of

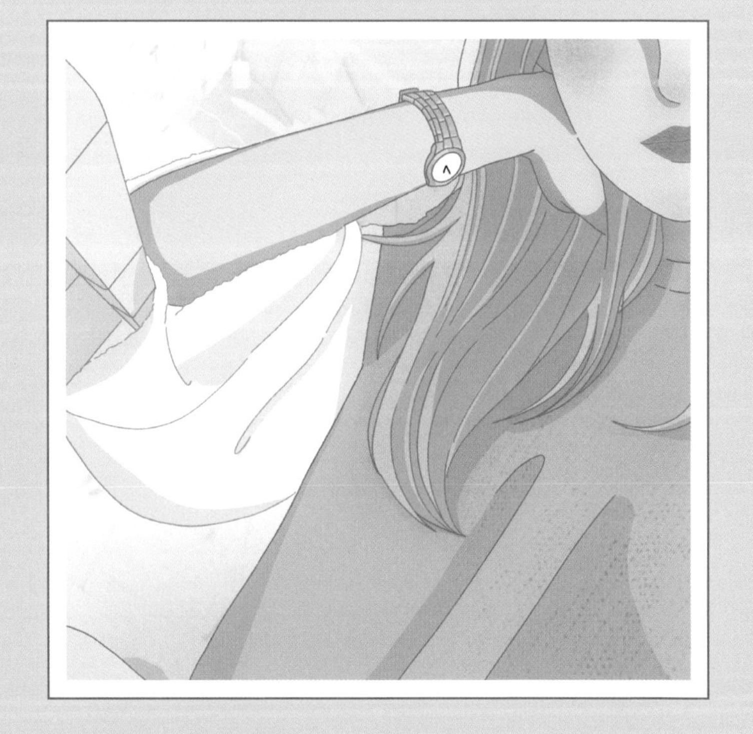

Listen to the audio track.

DAY 22

Are you thinking hard about whether or not to do something? Are you debating what to do next? If so, you can use "[something] + -을/를 [what you do] + -(으)ㄹ까 고민 중".
고민 literally means "concern" or "worry", but you can also use it to talk about something you are spending a lot of time making a decision about.

ex 핸드폰을 바꿀까 고민 중

thinking about changing my mobile phone

저녁을 시킬까 고민 중

thinking about ordering dinner

You can also use this phrase when writing in your weekly planner.

ex

Mon	Tue	Wed
골프를 배울까 고민 중 *thinking about learning how to play golf*		이사를 갈까 고민 중 *thinking about moving*

If you want to express that you are thinking about whether or not to do something, just add 말까 after -(으)ㄹ까.

ex 핸드폰을 바꿀까 말까 고민 중

thinking about whether or not to change my phone

저녁을 시킬까 말까 고민 중

thinking about whether or not to order dinner

이사를 갈까 말까 고민 중

thinking about whether or not to move

If you are deciding between two choices, you can add one more "[something] + -을/를 [what you do] + -(으)ㄹ까" before 고민 중.

ex

염색 = coloring, dye 하다 = to do 테니스 = tennis 배우다 = to learn

머리를 자를까 염색을 할까

고민 중 

thinking about whether to get my hair cut or colored

골프를 배울까 테니스를 배울까 고민 중

thinking about whether to learn golf or learn tennis

To write the phrases above in complete sentences, you can simply add -(이)다.

골프를 배울까 고민 중이다.
I am thinking about learning how to play golf.

이사를 갈까 고민 중이다.
I am thinking about moving.

핸드폰을 바꿀까 말까 고민 중이다.
I am thinking about whether or not to change my phone.

저녁을 시킬까 말까 고민 중이다.
I am thinking about whether or not to order dinner.

머리를 자를까 염색을 할까 고민 중이다.
I am thinking about whether to get my hair cut or colored.

What are you thinking about doing these days?
Write your own story and share it with us on social media!

....

Words you might need:

[N] + -을/를 [V] + -(으)ㄹ까 고민 중

N		V	
휴가	vacation, day off	쓰다	to use, to take
일	work, job	그만두다	to stop, to quit
커피	coffee	마시다	to drink

Weekly: Review

DAY 16.

나를 위한 [N]

DAY 17.

[N1] + -은/는 [N2] + -와/과 함께

DAY 20.

[Adj] + -(으)ㄴ/는 [N]

DAY 21.

[Adj] + -(으)ㄹ 것 같다.

앞에서 배운 패턴을 사용해, 다이어리의 위클리 페이지를 채워 보세요!

Fill in the weekly review page using the patterns you previously learned!

DAY 18.

[N] + -은/는 처음

DAY 19.

[V] + -(으)ㄹ 때 [Adj] + -(으)ㄴ/는 [N]

DAY 22.

[N] + -을/를 [V] + -(으)ㄹ까 고민 중

[V] + -고 있는 나 / me [V] + -ing

졸고 있는 나

me dozing off

Breakdown:

졸다
to doze off

-고 있다
to be -ing

-(으)ㄴ/는
suffix that makes the previous word into a modifier

나
I, me

 *Listen to the audio track.* .... 

Do you want to post a picture someone took of you doing something? If so, this is the expression for you. To explain what you are doing in the picture, you can use "[what you are doing in the picture] + -고 있는 나".

ex 웃고 있는 나

me smiling

핸드폰 보고 있는 나

me looking at my phone

If you add pictures of yourself to your journal, you can use this phrase as a caption.

ex

책 읽고 있는 나 *me reading a book*	
일하고 있는 나 *me working*	

You can explain the situation in more detail by using -에 or -에서.

ex

수업 시간에 = during class 회의 중에 = in the middle of a meeting 집에서 = at home

수업 시간에 졸고 있는 나

me dozing off during class

회의 중에 핸드폰 보고 있는 나

me looking at my phone in the middle of a meeting

집에서 일하고 있는 나

me working at home

If what you are doing in the picture contrasts with the situation you are in, you can use -(으)ㄴ/는데, which means "but", "whereas", or "when".

ex

친구가 넘어지다 = friend falls down

다른 사람들은 이야기하고 있다 = other people are talking

친구가 넘어졌는데 웃고 있는 나 

me smiling even though my friend fell down

다른 사람들은 이야기하고 있는데

책 읽고 있는 나

me reading a book while other people are talking

If you would like to write the phrases above in complete sentences, it is better to omit 나 and end the sentence with a verb to make the sentence sound natural.

ex

오늘 수업 시간에 졸고 있었다.

I was dozing off during class today.

오늘 회의 중에 핸드폰 보고 있었다.

I was looking at my phone in the middle of a meeting today.

오늘 친구가 넘어졌는데 웃고 있었다.

I was smiling even though my friend fell down today.

Do you have a photo of yourself taken while you are doing something?
Write your own story and share it with us on social media!

Words you might need:

[V] + -고 있는 나

V	
아이스크림을 고르다	to choose an ice cream flavor
사진을 찍다	to take a picture
음식을 기다리다	to wait for food

내가 [V] + -는 이유 / the reason why I [V]

내가 살이 찌는 이유

the reason why I gain weight

Breakdown:

내
I (The original form is 나, which changes to 내 when used before the subject marking particle -이/가.)

-이/가
subject marking particle

살
fat, flesh

찌다
to gain weight

-(으)ㄴ/는
suffix that makes the previous word into a modifier

이유
reason

 *Listen to the audio track.*

People often post a picture on social media that shows a reason for their behavior. The caption might be something like, "the reason why I do [something]", which helps their followers understand their behavior by looking at the picture. If you would like to make this kind of post as well, you can just write "내가 [what you do] + -는 이유".

ex 내가 새벽에 일어나는 이유

the reason why I wake up at dawn

내가 집에 일찍 오는 이유

the reason why I come home early

When you want to write a reason for doing something in your journal, you can also use this expression.

ex

내가 이 회사를 계속 다녀야 하는 이유 *the reason why I have to keep working for this company*	
내가 이 회사를 그만둘 수 없는 이유 *the reason why I cannot leave this company*	

In Korean, making a noun plural is often not necessary, but if you would like to indicate that there are a few reasons why you do something, you can add -들 to 이유.

ex 내가 이 회사를
계속 다녀야 하는 이유들
the reasons why I have to keep working for this company

내가 이 회사를
그만둘 수 없는 이유들
the reasons why I cannot leave this company

If you would like to write the phrases above in complete sentences, use 이것이 -(이)다 to add "this is" to your sentences. 이것이 can also be replaced with 이게, the shortened form of 이것이.

이게 내가 살이 찌는 이유다.
This is the reason why I gain weight.

이게 내가 새벽에 일어나는 이유다.
This is the reason why I wake up at dawn.

이게 내가 집에 일찍 오는 이유다.
This is the reason why I come home early.

이게 내가 이 회사를 계속 다녀야 하는 이유들이다.
These are the reasons why I have to keep working for this company.

이게 내가 이 회사를 그만둘 수 없는 이유들이다.
These are the reasons why I cannot leave this company.

Are there reasons for certain behaviors of yours that you want to share with others? Write your own story and share it with us on social media!

....

Words you might need: 내가 [V] + -는 이유

V			
일을 열심히 하다	to work hard	혼자 살다	to live by oneself
일찍 출근하다	to go to work early		

25

DAY

벌써 [N] + -(이)네. / Wow, it is already [N].

벌써 12월이네.

Wow, it is already December.

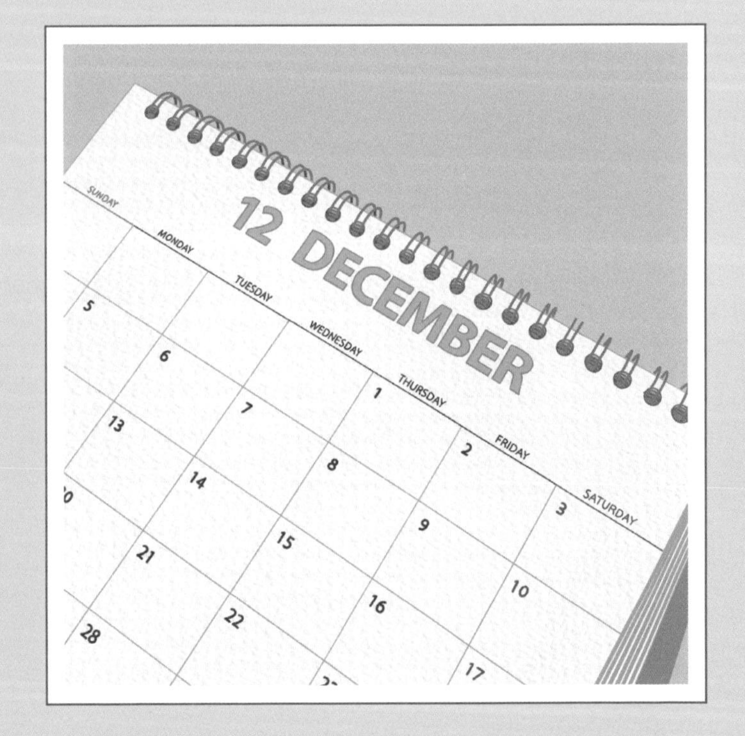

Breakdown:

벌써
already

12월
December

-이다
to be

-네
verb ending that expresses that the speaker is impressed or surprised

Listen to the audio track.

Have you ever been surprised by how quickly time passed? When you realize that time has flown by, you can express this feeling by using the expression "벌써 [something] + -(이)네".

ex 벌써 여덟 살이네.

Wow, he/she is already eight years old.

벌써 끝이네.

Wow, it is already the end.

You can also use this sentence structure when writing in a journal.

ex

벌써 수요일이네. *Wow, it is already Wednesday.*	
벌써 졸업이네. *Wow, it is already graduation.*	

The sentences above have no subject. To make your meaning clearer, you can add a subject to each sentence.

ex
우리 아들 = my son 오늘 = today 우리 = we

우리 아들이 벌써 여덟 살이네.

Wow, my son is already eight years old.

오늘이 벌써 수요일이네.

Wow, today is already Wednesday.

우리가 벌써 졸업이네.

Wow, we are already graduating.

You can also move **벌써** to the beginning of the sentence.

벌써 우리 아들이 여덟 살이네. 

Wow, my son is already eight years old.

벌써 오늘이 수요일이네.

Wow, today is already Wednesday.

벌써 우리가 졸업이네.

Wow, we are already graduating.

You can also add a verb.

ex 벌써 12월이 되었네.

Wow, it has already become December.

우리 아들이 벌써
여덟 살이 되었네.

Wow, my son has already become eight years old.

벌써 끝났네.

Wow, it already ended.

우리가 벌써 졸업을 하네.

Wow, we are already graduating.

Have you recently experienced time passing quickly?
Write your own story and share it with us on social media!

Words you might need:

벌써 [N] + -(이)네.

N			
봄	spring	가을	fall
여름	summer	겨울	winter

26 DAY

[N] + -이/가 별로 [Adj] + -네. / [N] is not very [Adj].

사람이 별로 없네.

There are not very many people.

Breakdown:

사람
person, people

-이/가
subject marking particle

별로
(not) very, particularly

없다
to not have, to not be there

-네
verb ending that expresses that the speaker is impressed or surprised

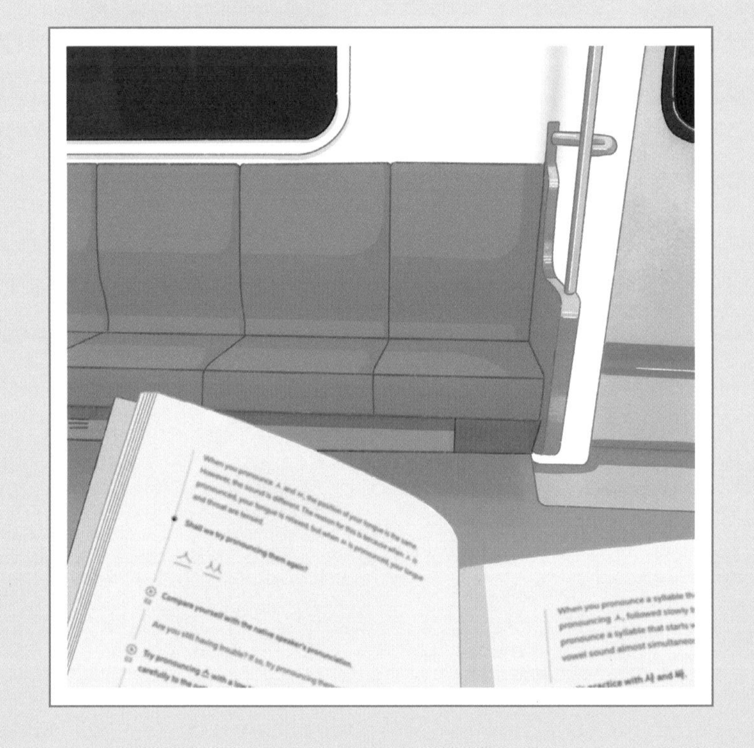

 *Listen to the audio track.*

When you want to say that something is "not particularly" a certain way, you can use the expression "[something] + -이/가 별로 [how it is] + -네". 별로 means "particularly" or "very" and is always used with a negative expression. The ending -네 implies that you are realizing or acknowledging something for the first time.

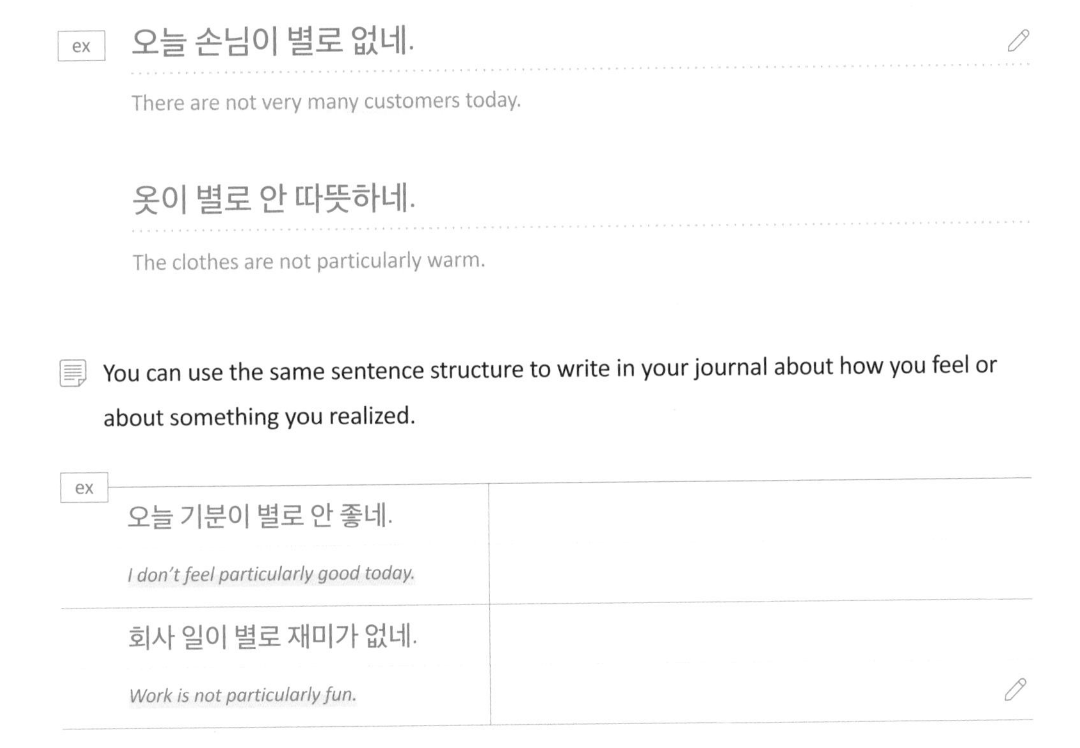

The phrase 생각보다 means "than I thought" or "than I expected" and goes well with this expression.

ex 생각보다 사람이 별로 없네.

There are less people than I expected.

생각보다 오늘 손님이

별로 없네.

Compared to what I expected, there are far fewer customers today.

생각보다 옷이 별로

안 따뜻하네.

The clothes are less warm than I expected.

You can also use -(으)ㄴ/는데 to add background information that explains why you expected something to be different.

ex

주말이다 = it is the weekend

두껍다 = to be thick

안 좋은 일도 없다 = there are no bad things, there is also nothing bad

들어오고 싶은 회사에 들어오다 = to join the company that one wants to join

주말인데 사람이 별로 없네.

It is the weekend, but there are not very many people.

옷이 두꺼운데 별로
안 따뜻하네.

The clothes are thick, but they are not particularly warm.

안 좋은 일도 없는데
오늘 기분이 별로 안 좋네.

Nothing bad happened, but I don't feel particularly good today.

들어오고 싶은 회사에 들어왔는데
회사 일이 별로 재미가 없네.

I joined the company that I wanted to join, but work is not particularly fun.

What is something that turned out to be different from what you had expected? Write your own story and share it with us on social media!

....

Words you might need:

[N] + -이/가 별로 [Adj] + -네.

N		Adj	
차	car	없다	to not have, to not be there
짐	load, baggage	많지 않다	to not be a lot
할 일	work to do	안 많다	to not be a lot

[V] + -(으)ㄹ 수 있을까? / Will I/we be able to [V]?

오늘 집에 갈 수 있을까?

Will I be able to go home today?

Breakdown:

오늘
today

집
house, home

-에
to

가다
to go

-(으)ㄹ 수 있다
can, to be able to

-(으)ㄹ까?
I wonder

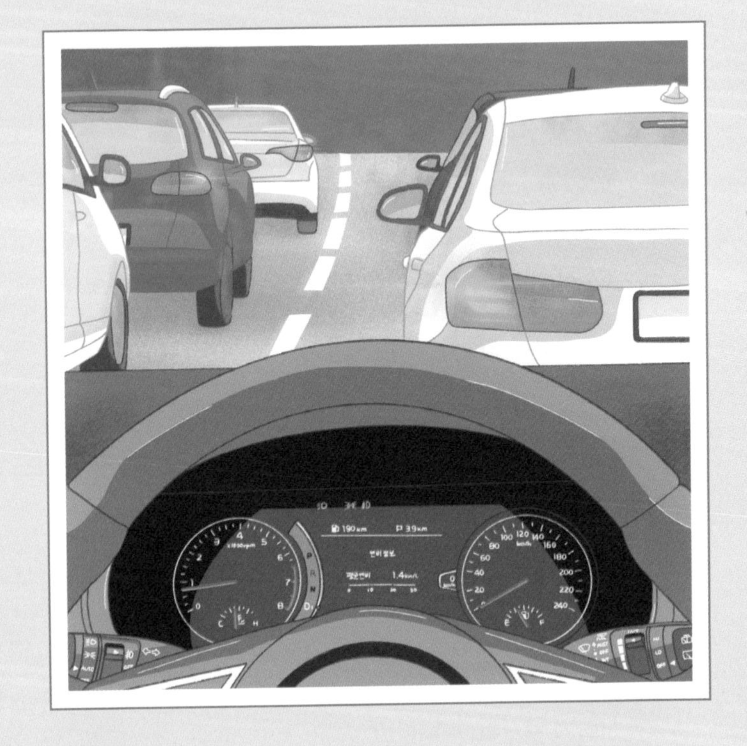

 *Listen to the audio track.*

Are you wondering if you will be able to do something? Whether you are feeling doubtful or just curious about the possibility of something, you can use "[what you do] + -(으)ㄹ 수 있을까?"

ex 이거 다 끝낼 수 있을까?

Will I be able to finish all of this?

일찍 퇴근할 수 있을까?

Will I be able to leave work early?

여기 다시 올 수 있을까?

Will I be able to come here again?

You can also use "[what you do] + -(으)ㄹ 수 있을까?" in your journal when you are not confident about or doubt your ability to do something.

ex

시험을 잘 볼 수 있을까? *Will I be able to do well on the exam?*	
시험에 합격할 수 있을까? *Will I be able to pass the exam?*	

한국에 다시 갈 수 있을까?	
Will I be able to go to Korea again?	

If you would like to explain the background to your wondering, you can use -(으)ㄴ/는데, which means "but", "while" or "whereas".

ex

아직 이것밖에 못 하다 = to have done only this much so far

일이 많다 = to have a lot of work

공부 많이 못 하다 = to not be able to study a lot

아직 이것밖에 못 했는데,

오늘 집에 갈 수 있을까?

I have done only this much so far. Will I be able to go home today?

일이 많은데,

일찍 퇴근할 수 있을까?

I have a lot of work to do. Will I be able to leave work early?

공부 많이 못 했는데,

시험을 잘 볼 수 있을까?

I wasn't able to study a lot. Will I be able to do well on the exam?

If you are wondering if you will be able to do something under a certain condition, you can use -(으)면.

ex

오늘 하루 종일 하다 = to do it all day long today

미국으로 돌아가다 = to go back to the US

공부 열심히 하다 = to study hard

오늘 하루 종일 하면

이거 다 끝낼 수 있을까?

If I do it all day long today, will I be able to finish all of this?

미국으로 돌아가면

여기 다시 올 수 있을까?

If I go back to the US, will I be able to come here again?

공부 열심히 하면 시험에 합격할 수 있을까?

If I study hard, will I be able to pass the exam?

Is there anything that you are wondering if you will be able to do?
Write your own story and share it with us on social media!

Words you might need:

[V] + -(으)ㄹ 수 있을까?

V	
다 먹다	to eat it all
혼자 하다	to do it by oneself
잘하다	to do it well; to be good at

28

DAY

[V] + -(으)세요. / [V] (imperative).

주말 잘 보내세요.

Have a good weekend.

Breakdown:

주말
weekend

잘
well

보내다
to spend

-(으)세요
imperative ending

 *Listen to the audio track.*

If you want to write greetings like "have a good weekend" on social media, you can write "[what you wish for people] + -(으)세요".

ex 좋은 하루 보내세요.

Have a good day.

새해 복 많이 받으세요.

(lit.) Receive a lot of luck in the new year.

You won't use this form when writing in your journal or planner, but you can use it in an email or letter.

ex

안녕하세요*. *Hello.*	
감기 조심하세요. *Be careful not to catch a cold.*	

* For those of you who know 안녕하세요 only as a set expression, 안녕하세요 is actually a combination of 안녕하다 (= to be peaceful, to be healthy) and -(으)세요. Its original meaning is, "Are you well?"

If you would like to add "everyone" when you write greetings on social media, you can use 여러분, either at the beginning or at the end of the sentence.

ex 여러분, 주말 잘 보내세요.

Everyone, have a good weekend.

여러분, 좋은 하루 보내세요.

Everyone, have a good day.

새해 복 많이 받으세요, 여러분.

Happy New Year, everyone.

If you are an employee managing your company's social media account, you will probably make a lot of imperative sentences in addition to greetings.

ex 오늘까지 신청하세요.

Apply for it by the end of today.

지금 예약하세요.

Make a reservation now.

Since "[what you ask people to do] + -(으)세요" is quite a direct way to tell someone what to do, it is more polite to use "[what you would like people to do] + -아/어/여 주세요" when you say what you would like your followers to do.

ex 확인해 주세요.

Please check.

들러 주세요.

Please stop by.

What greetings do you want to write to your followers?
Write your own story and share it with us on social media!

Words you might need:

[V] + -(으)세요.

V	
안녕히 계시다	to stay in peace (said to someone when you leave)
안녕히 주무시다	to sleep in peace
안녕히 다녀오다	to go and come back in peace

[V/Adj] + -아/어/여요. / [V/Adj] + -(스)ㅂ니다.
/ I/we [V/Adj].

결혼해요. / 결혼합니다.

We are getting married.

Breakdown:

결혼하다
to get married

-아/어/여요
polite and informal verb ending

-(스)ㅂ니다
polite and formal verb ending

* 결혼해요 and 결혼합니다 are both technically in the present tense, but they can also refer to something that will happen in the future.

 *Listen to the audio track.*

.... 

Do you often need to announce news or events, or address a large group of people on your social media account? If so, you will often have to write sentences that end with polite verb endings. There are two polite verb endings: -아/어/여요 and -(스)ㅂ니다. -(스)ㅂ니다 is the more formal of the two, but people often use a mix of both in their posts.

ex 감사해요. / 감사합니다.

Thank you.

죄송해요. / 죄송합니다.

I am sorry.

Since you only use -아/어/여요 and -(스)ㅂ니다 when talking to somebody else, you will not use them when writing in your journal. However, if you have a blog, you will often use these two forms because you are writing directly to your readers.

ex

돌아가요. / 돌아갑니다. *I am going back.*	
떠나요. / 떠납니다. *I am leaving.*	

You can also add a subject to the sentence.

ex

저희 결혼해요.

저희 결혼합니다.

We are getting married.

저는 돌아가요.

저는 돌아갑니다.

I am going back.

저는 떠나요.

저는 떠납니다.

I am leaving.

You don't need to add a subject to fixed expressions like "thank you" and "I am sorry". Instead, a reason is often added using -아/어/여서.

ex

축하해 주시다* = to congratulate 불편을 드리다 = to cause inconvenience

* -(으)시- is an honorific suffix, so 주시다 is the honorific version of 주다.

축하해 주셔서 감사해요.

축하해 주셔서 감사합니다.

Thank you for congratulating me.

불편을 드려서 죄송해요.

불편을 드려서 죄송합니다.

I am sorry for causing you inconvenience.

What would you like to say to your followers?
Write your own story and share it with us on social media!

Words you might need: [V/Adj] + -아/어/여요. / [V/Adj] + -(스)ㅂ니다.

V/Adj			
행복하다	to be happy	추천하다	to recommend
사랑하다	to love		

[V/Adj] + -았/었/였어요. / [V/Adj] + -았/었/였습니다.
/ I/we [V/Adj].

행복한 생일이었어요. / 행복한 생일이었습니다.

I had a happy birthday.

Breakdown:

행복하다
to be happy

-(으)ㄴ/는
suffix that makes the previous word into a modifier

생일
birthday

-(이)다
to be

-았/었/였-
past tense suffix

-아/어/여요
polite and informal verb ending

-(스)ㅂ니다
polite and formal verb ending

 *Listen to the audio track.*

Continuing from Day 29, we are looking at expressions that you can use when writing directly to your readers. We practiced making present tense sentences on Day 29, so now let's practice making past tense sentences using "[what you do / how you feel] + -았/었/였어요" and "[what you do / how you feel] + -았/었/였습니다".

ex

오늘 즐거웠어요.

오늘 즐거웠습니다.

I had fun today.

커피 잘 마셨어요.

커피 잘 마셨습니다.

Thank you for the coffee.

Like we mentioned in the previous chapter, you can only use -았/었/였어요 and -았/었/였습니다 when talking directly to somebody. You will not use these forms when writing in your journal — just when writing a blog post, letter, or email.

ex

블로그 열었어요.
블로그 열었습니다.

I opened a blog.

만나서 반가웠어요. 만나서 반가웠습니다.	
It was nice meeting you.	

When writing several sentences together, people often switch back and forth between -아/어/여요 and -(스)ㅂ니다 to avoid repetition.

ex

선물 감사하다 = to thank for the present

집에 오다 = to come home

오랜만에 돌아오다 = to come back after a long time away

선물 감사했어요.

행복한 생일이었습니다. 

Thank you for the present. I had a happy birthday.

저는 집에 왔어요.

오늘 즐거웠습니다.

I'm home. I had fun today.

블로그 열었습니다.

오랜만에 돌아왔어요.

I opened a blog. I came back after a long time away.

What would you like to say to your followers?

Write your own story and share it with us on social media!

Words you might need: [V/Adj] + -았/었/였어요. / [V/Adj] + -았/었/였습니다.

V/Adj	
잘 먹다	to eat well
끝나다	to end, to finish
잘 도착하다	to arrive well

Weekly: Review

DAY 23.

[V] + -고 있는 나

DAY 24.

내가 [V] + -는 이유

DAY 27.

[V] + -(으)ㄹ 수 있을까?

DAY 28.

[V] + -(으)세요.

앞에서 배운 패턴을 사용해, 다이어리의 위클리 페이지를 채워 보세요!

Fill in the weekly review page using the patterns you previously learned!

DAY 25.

벌써 [N] + -(이)네.

DAY 26.

[N] + -이/가 별로 [Adj] + -네.

DAY 29.

[V/Adj] + -아/어/여요.

/ [V/Adj] + -(스)ㅂ니다.

DAY 30.

[V/Adj] + -았/었/였어요.

/ [V/Adj] + -았/었/였습니다.

Glossary

-이	a suffix used after a name ending in a final consonant
12월	December
1999년	the year 1999
1일	the first day of the month; one day
2월	February
8시	8 o'clock
가다	to go
가을	fall (the season)
가족	family
가족사진	family picture
감기	a cold
감사하다	to appreciate, to be thankful for
강아지	dog, puppy
거	thing * This is a casual and colloquial form of the original form 것.
걷다	to talk
검사	check, examination
게임	game
겨울	winter
결혼식	wedding
결혼하다	to get married
계속	continuously
계시다	to be (honorific), to stay (honorific)
고르다	to choose
고민	thinking, worry, concern
고양이	cat
골프	golf
공부	study
공원	park
과자	snack
과제	assignment
괜찮다	to be all right, to be okay
교수님	professor
권	counter for books
귀엽다	to be cute
그리다	to draw
그림	drawing, picture
그림책	picture book

그만두다	to stop, to quit, to leave
글씨	handwriting
금요일	Friday
기다리다	to wait
기분	feeling, mood
길다	to be long
김치	kimchi
깨끗하다	to be clean
꽃	flower
끝	end, finish
끝나다	to be done, to be over, to end, to finish
끝내다	to finish
나	I, me
나가다	to go out
날씨	weather
남자 친구	boyfriend
남편	husband
내	I * The original form of 내 is 나. 나 changes to 내 when used before the subject marking particle -이/가.
내다	to make (a test or quiz)

내일	tomorrow
너무	very, really, too, so
넘어지다	to fall down
년	year
노래	song
노래하다	to sing
놀다	to hang out, to play
놀이공원	theme park
누나	older sister (used by men)
느끼하다	to be greasy, to be rich
다	all
다녀오다	to go and come back
다니다	to attend, to work for
다른	other
다시	again
다음	next
다이어트	being on a diet
답답하다	to be frustrated, to be frustrating, to be stuffy
대학교	university
덥다	to be hot

데이트	a date
도넛	doughnut
도서관	library
도착하다	to arrive
돌아가다	to go back
돌아오다	to come back
동네	neighborhood
동생	younger brother/sister
되다	to become
두껍다	to be thick
드디어	finally
드리다	to give (honorific)
듣다	to take (a class)
들르다	to stop by
들어오다	to come in, to join
등산	hiking
따뜻하다	to be warm
딸	daughter
때	the time, the moment
떠나다	to leave, to depart
똑똑하다	to be smart
라면	ramyeon
마시다	to drink
마트	supermarket
만나다	to meet
만들다	to make
많다	to be a lot
많이	a lot * This is the adverb form of **많다**.
말	talk, words, conversation
말다	to not do
맛있다	to be yummy, to be delicious
머리	hair
먹다	to eat
멋있다	to be cool
메시지	message
목걸이	necklace
목표	goal
몰래	secretly, in secret
못	cannot + V
못생기다	to be ugly

무섭다	to be scary
문자	text
미국	United States
바꾸다	to change
바다	ocean
바쁘다	to be busy
반갑다	to be glad to see someone
받다	to receive
발표	presentation
방	room
방학	school vacation
배고프다	to be hungry
배우다	to learn
백화점	department store
버리다	to throw away
번째	counter for ordinal numbers
벌써	already
베이글	bagel
별로	(not) very, particularly
병원	hospital

보내다	to send; to spend
보다	to watch, to see, to look; to take (an exam)
복	luck
봄	spring
부산	Busan
부지런하다	to be diligent
불편	inconvenience
불편하다	to be inconvenient
브랜드	brand
블로그	blog
비	rain
비싸다	to be expensive
비행기	flight
빵	bread
사다	to buy
사람	person, people
사람들	people *-들 is a plural suffix.
사랑하다	to love
사무실	office

사진	picture, photo
산책	walk, stroll
산책하다	to take a walk
살(1)	fat
살(2)	counter for age
살다	to live
새벽	dawn
새우	shrimp
새해	new year
생각	thought
생일	birthday
서울	Seoul
선물	present, gift
선생님	teacher
선택	choice
성공	success
성공하다	to succeed
세우다	to set (a plan or goal)
손	hand
손님	customer
쇼핑	shopping
쇼핑몰	shopping mall
수다	talk, chat
수술	surgery
수업	class
수업 시간	class time
수영장	swimming pool
수요일	Wednesday
숙제	homework
숙제하다	to do one's homework
스무	twenty (native Korean number, modifying form)
스페인어	Spanish
시	o'clock
시간	hour, time
시끄럽다	to be noisy
시작	start, beginning
시작하다	to start
시키다	to order
시험	exam
식당	restaurant

식사	meal
신발	shoes
신청하다	to apply for, to register
쓰다[1]	to write
쓰다[2]	to use, to take
아	Ah (a sound you make when surprised or embarrassed)
아내	wife
아들	son
아르바이트	part-time job
아빠	dad
아이들	children * -들 is a plural suffix.
아이스크림	ice cream
아직	so far
아침	morning; breakfast
안	to not + A/V
안녕하다	to be peaceful, to be healthy
안녕히	in peace
어렵다	to be difficult
어제	yesterday

언니	older sister (used by women)
엄마	mom
없다	to not have, to not be there
여기	here
여덟	eight (native Korean number)
여러분	everyone
여름	summer
여행	travel, trip
역시	of course
연극	play
연습	practice
연어	salmon
열다	to hold; to open
열심히	hard, diligently, enthusiastically
염색	coloring, dye
영화	movie
영화관	movie theater
예쁘다	to be pretty
예약하다	to make a reservation
오늘	today

오다	to come
오래되다	to be old
오랜만	after a while, after a long time
오렌지	orange (fruit)
오빠	older brother (used by women)
올라가다	to go up; to mount
올해	this year
옷	clothes
외식	eating out
외출	going out
요리	cooking, dish
요리하다	to cook
요즘	these days
우리	my, we
우유	milk
운동	exercise
운전	driving
운전하다	to drive
움직이다	to move
웃기다	to be funny

웃다	to smile, to laugh
원피스	dress
월	month
월요일	Monday
위하다	to be for
음식	food
의자	chair
이(1)	teeth
이(2)	this * This word is the adjective form of 이거.
이거	this one, this, these * This is a casual and colloquial form of the original form 이것.
이것	this one, this, these
이번	this time
이사	move
이야기하다	to talk
이유	reason
일(1)	work, job; thing
일(2)	day
일기	diary entry
일어나다	to get up, to wake up

일찍	early
일하다	to work
읽다	to read
입다	to wear, to put on
있다	to be
자다	to sleep
자르다	to cut
자전거	bike
작년	last year
작다	to be small
잔	cup, glass
잘	well, skillfully, properly
잘하다	to do it well; to be good at
장	counter for pictures
재미	fun
재미있다	to be fun, to be enjoyable
재밌다	to be enjoyable, to be fun * This is a shortened word for **재미있다**.
저	I, me (honorific)
저녁	dinner
저녁 시간	evening, dinner time

저희	we, our (honorific)
전	before
점심	lunch
점심시간	lunchtime
정말	really
제일	most
제주도	Jeju Island
조심하다	to be careful
조용하다	to be quiet
조카	nephew/niece
졸다	to doze off
졸업	graduation
좋다	to be good
좋아하다	to like
죄송하다	to be sorry
주	week
주말	weekend
주무시다	to sleep (honorific)
주스	juice
준비	preparation

준비하다	to plan
중	in the middle of
중간	the middle, center
즐겁다	to be happy, to be fun
지금	now
지난	last
지루하다	to be boring
짐	load, baggage
집	house, home
찌다	to gain weight
찍다	to take (a picture)
차	car
책	book
책상	desk
처음	first
청소	cleaning
추천	recommendation
추천하다	to recommend
축제	festival
축하하다	to congratulate

출근	going to work
출근하다	to go to work
출발	departure
춤	dance
춤추다	to dance
춥다	to be cold
치료	medical treatment
치킨	fried chicken
친구	friend
카메라	camera
카페	cafe
커피	coffee
케이크	cake
코트	coat
콘서트	concert
콜라	cola
크림치즈	cream cheese
타다	to get on, to take (a vehicle)
테니스	tennis
통통하다	to be chubby

통화하다	to talk over the telephone
퇴근하다	to leave work
파랗다	to be blue (the color)
파스타	pasta
파티	party
편지	letter
표정	facial expression
프렌치프라이	french fries
프로그램	program
피곤하다	to be tired, to be tiring
피자	pizza
하늘	sky
하다	to do
하루	day
하루 종일	all day long
하이힐	high-heeled shoes
학교	school
학기	semester
한	a, an, one
한국	Korean (when used as a modifier)
한국어	Korean language
함께	together
합격하다	to pass
핸드폰	mobile phone
햄버거	hamburger
행복하다	to be happy
형	older brother (used by men)
혼자	by oneself, alone
홍대	Hongdae
화내다	to get angry
확인하다	to check
회사	company
회사 사람	coworker
회사 일	work (in an office)
회의	meeting
회의하다	to discuss, to have a meeting
후	after
휴가	vacation, day off
힘들다	to be tough

TTMIK Book Audio App

Download our app TTMIK: Audio to listen to all the audio and video tracks from our book conveniently on your phone! The app is available for free on both iOS and Android. Search for TTMIK: Audio in your app store.

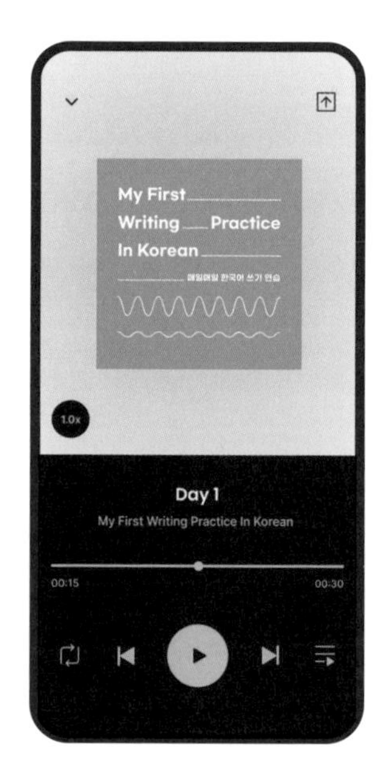